Tired Feelings and How to Master Them

Books by Donald A. Laird and Eleanor C. Laird

Tired Feelings and How to Master Them
Techniques for Efficient Remembering
Sound Ways to Sound Sleep
The Techniques of Delegating
Practical Sales Psychology
Practical Business Psychology
Sizing Up People
The Technique of Getting Things Done
The Technique of Building Personal Leadership
Published by Harper & Brothers:
Increasing Personal Efficiency
Published by Funk & Wagnalls Company:
The Strategy of Handling Children
Published by American Bankers Association:
Human Relations in Banking

TIRED
FEELINGS
and how to
MASTER
THEM
A Practical Summary of Techniques for Home and Business

Dr. Donald A. Laird and Eleanor C. Laird

McGRAW-HILL BOOK COMPANY, INC.

New York Toronto London

TIRED FEELINGS AND HOW TO MASTER THEM

Library of Congress Catalog Card Number: 60-16917

First Edition

35985

Preface

We daresay there are few other things people have so much of, and know so little about, as their tired feelings. These feelings have a pervading effect upon the will to work, and on the enjoyment of life in general. We believe they are worth understanding.

The purpose of this book is to report the current teachings of experts who are qualified to help the average person understand his tired feelings and what to do about them. We have tried to present the information in terms and with a variety of examples the average executive, white-collar worker, industrial engineer, or housewife will find interesting and meaningful for his or her own life and work.

The focus is on office and factory workers who do not do heavy physical work, but get tired. And, since housewives and professional people also often feel tired without having done heavy work, examples from those categories are included.

This book deals primarily with the very personal experience of feeling tired, not with "the state of fatigue." This is in line with scientific investigators' change in emphasis which is summarized as The New View in Chapter 1.

The material has been collected from scientific and historical sources. From the latter we have gleaned examples from the lives of distinguished people which appear to illustrate or apply some of the scientists' findings, and may make it easier to comprehend and remember the findings.

The scientific findings have been combed from clinical experiences in rehabilitating people who were handicapped by feeling tired, and from laboratory experiments which probed the basic biological factors—or physicochemical and neuroglandular correlates—involved in tired feelings. We have not used material from the sales literature of firms which offer fatigue-reducing equipment.

Although The New View has come to dominate the field, research studies of tired feelings are not numerous. Much of the information has come as a by-product of researches on other problems. As a consequence the information is still fragmentary in some areas, and we are very far from having an exact scientific account of tired feelings. There are enough verified findings, however, to draw a general sketch with a minimum of speculation. Such a sketch, of which we hope this book is an example, will provide the employer, and the individual himself, with a much more sound basis for dealing with tired feelings than has previously been available for the general reader.

In attempting to give a simple account of a complex topic, we have been dependent upon the cooperation of the researchers cited to check the accuracy of our nontechnical simplifications of their findings and recommendations. We are deeply indebted to the following who have given us that assistance or permission to quote from their work:

Frank N. Allan, Roger G. Bannister, S. Howard Bartley, Edwin G. Boring, Lucien A. Brouha, Edward A. Burkhardt, Raymond B. Cattell, H. Harrison Clarke, David B. Dill, Jack W. Dunlap, O. G. Edholm, Geoffrey E. Ffrench, Gordon

N. French, George T. Hauty, Edgar M. Haverland, Frederick Herzberg, S. Richardson Hill, Abram Kardiner, Edward A. Kempf, Benjamin Kissin, Theodore G. Klumpp, Peter H. Knapp, Henry P. Laughlin, Otto Lowenstein, Sir Heneage Ogilvie, Robert B. Payne, Richard G. Pearson, Theron G. Randolph, David Riesman, John Romano, Robert S. Schwab, Harley C. Shands, W. B. Spaulding, Frederic Speer, Muriel H. Stern, John W. Thibaut, Robert L. Thorndike, and Robert S. Woodworth.

For students, industrial engineers, and others who may wish to consult the original researches, the bibliography at the end of the book lists the relevant publications of the scientists whose names are mentioned in the text. In addition, a list of readings is included for those who want to dig more deeply into the subject; this list is selective, including only those books which are regarded by qualified experts as being on a firm scientific footing.

The reader who is in a hurry can get the gist of this book, with at least a minimum of practical understanding, by reading the first two and the last two chapters.

Donald A. Laird
Eleanor C. Laird
Morainewood-on-Wabash

CONTENTS

CHAPTER 1

The new view of tired feelings

1. The age-old double-barreled question

"Why do we get tired. . . . What can we do about it?"

That doubled-barreled question is probably as old as mankind. It still pesters individuals and puzzles employers. Now, however, we are on the way toward some useful answers which will enable people to get more things done without feeling too dragged out by the doing—answers that can help us master tired feelings instead of being mastered by them.

Employers have been concerned because tired feelings often (but not always) cut into output, or lower the quality of work. Employers have been on the defensive because tired workers frequently put all the blame for their tired feelings on their work.

1

The individual has been concerned because his tired feelings seem to hold him back, whether he works for an employer or himself. If he feels tired too often he may not make good on the job; the possibility of failure can make him anxious and insecure—and in turn the anxiety and insecurity make the tired feelings worse, in a vicious circle. In addition, tired feelings often take the zest out of life—"he comes home from work and just sits to rest up."

Too many people are too tired too much of the time in spite of everything they have tried to cut down tired feelings. Surveys show that any time of the working day at least one person out of four feels so tired he stops, or wants desperately to stop what he is doing, or can't bring himself to start what he should start.

What can be done about this? A great deal, but only if we understand the language used by tired feelings and can figure out what they are trying to tell us.

2. Little accomplished by the old view

"I don't see how our workers have a right to get tired," a man from an insurance company said at an office managers' conference.

"Our work is light; the medical department says it does not use up enough energy to tire out a fly. But to play safe we have coffee breaks, air conditioning, acoustical ceilings, posture chairs, and music every alternate quarter hour. For years we've been easy marks for any new gimmick that might solve the problem. Yet our girls still get tired out, or at least they claim they do, and we've had a 40-hour week for years. Will you men tell me what else we can do that might lick the problem?"

Here are some of the suggestions he received. They are

typical of the blind groping practical men have had to engage in because they lacked basic information about tired feelings.

The office manager of a cotton mill said: "There's nothing you can do, because what tires the girls out is their dates the night before. Some of them are serious and don't date every night, but the serious ones tire themselves out doing housework, or taking night courses. If we could supervise their after-work hours, the way they used to do in the textile industry at Lowell, we wouldn't have so many girls with tired feelings on the job."

The office manager from a stamping firm added: "It's because we hire women and girls. You can bet it was different in the old days when offices were filled with men and brass cuspidors. Everyone knows that women tire out quickly—look at the way our wives complain about housework when the house is full of labor-saving conveniences. Some folks are simply born tired, that's the trouble."

From a public-utility manager: "Maybe it isn't real tiredness, but a false feeling they would forget if you put them to work on quotas that kept them humping."

Hopefully, from a credit-bureau manager: "Wonder if it would help if you gave them vitamin pills?"

The office manager from an air line said: "I've always suspected that a lot of it [tired feelings] was just laziness. If we had some test that would weed out the lazy ones in the employment office, we wouldn't have to coddle the force with fancy chairs, ceilings full of holes to absorb noise, and music to keep them from dragging their feet."

Not much help from these comments. And most of the ideas expressed were as wrong as the notion that white-collar workers have no right to feel tired at easy desk jobs. Yet those office managers' ideas are typical of the prevailing narrow view which does not see enough of the whole picture to get the real problem in focus.

Until recently there was little that a company, or individual, could use in the battle against tired feelings except homemade notions, pet theories, and passing fads. Witness the large sums business has spent on equipment to make work easier and comfortable in the hope that it would lessen the "fatigue problem." But the problem continues, as everybody concerned knows to his regret.

3. How researchers expanded the view

The future can be much better. New information has broadened the view and revealed a perspective which now, so to speak, gives a third dimension to our picture of how to deal with tired feelings.

Research on fatigue got under way in earnest only after World War I, when special laboratories were set up and commissions appointed to dig for facts. Some of their first findings were hailed as cures for tired feelings, but they proved to be duds when investigated further.

An example is the lactic-acid theory, which was one of the first to rise. Lactic acid does, of course, play a role in the body. It is made from blood sugar (glycogen) as it is used in muscle contractions. According to the early view, lactic acid accumulated as work went on, and it had a toxic effect which brought on muscle tiredness. Lactic acid produced in the right arm would spread, so the theory said, to muscles that were not working and make them tired. Some faddists went overboard and decided they needed only an antiacid diet to avoid tired feelings—how silly can people get!

It is now clearly established, however, that lactic acid does not accumulate except in cases of the heaviest exertion. The white-collar worker never accumulates it in his work. Most of the small amount produced by his muscle activity is quickly converted back into energy-rich compounds the muscle can use at once.

This is typical of the fate of many of the early findings. Many investigators lost heart and some of the larger laboratories and commissions were shut down. The research came to a standstill, waiting for a shove in a new direction.

The shove can be dated 1947 when *Fatigue and Impairment in Man,* by Drs. S. H. Bartley and Eloise Chute was published. In it they demonstrated the futility of the Old View and gave a new conception of tiredness to guide research in new directions. Since then the scientific conception of tiring out has been revolutionized. In this book we will piece together many findings from various fields of science to give a practical, though still not complete, answer to the double-barreled question "Why do we get tired.... What can we do about it?"

Two streams of research have made this possible. Although these streams are trickles rather than torrents, they have produced a great deal of exciting information about what can be done to prevent tired feelings, or to make them less of a handicap in those instances where they can't be avoided. These are the streams in which those office managers should have fished for their answers.

4. Biomedical scientists deepened the view

One stream of research has been flowing from the biomedical sciences, represented by:

Physiologists' researches on muscle function
Biochemists' findings on energy-rich processes during muscle
    activity

Neurophysiologists' discoveries about the role of nerves, especially the autonomic nerves

Endocrinologists' studies of the role of the ductless glands

Many useful discoveries have been made from these approaches. Most of this research has been done in the laboratory, or clinic. A few large firms, however, have portable laboratories for studying people while at work on production jobs.

Physiatrists (physicians who specialize in restoring or improving muscle function) have applied the findings of the

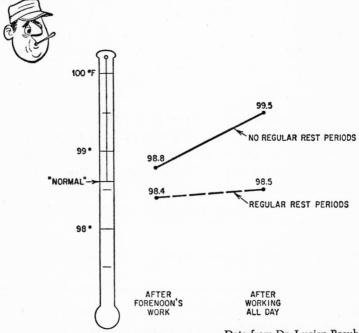

100 °F

99.5
NO REGULAR REST PERIODS

99°

98.8

"NORMAL"→

98.5
98.4
REGULAR REST PERIODS

98°

AFTER
FORENOON'S
WORK

AFTER
WORKING
ALL DAY

Data from Dr. Lucien Brouha

Heavy work in the smelter caused less rise in body temperature when the men had regular rest periods (Output remained the same)

biomedical researchers and devised many techniques for getting the most out of muscles with least stress and strain.

The first two chartoons illustrate some biomedical findings about tried feelings from a study of men who were doing hard work on their regular jobs.

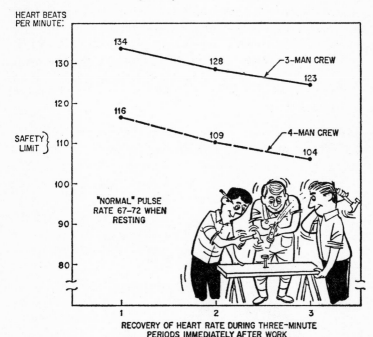

RECOVERY OF HEART RATE DURING THREE-MINUTE
PERIODS IMMEDIATELY AFTER WORK

Data from Dr. Lucien Brouha

Adding one man to the crew brought their exertion down to safe limits (The crew was doing fairly heavy work)

• *These are the first of the visual aids in this book. Each has an important practical message. The chartoons are usually not discussed further in the text, so each should be studied for the story it tells about some aspect of tired feelings.*

5. *Behavioral scientists widened the view*

The other stream of research has been flowing from the behavioral sciences. This is the more youthful stream, but has been growing in importance. It is represented by:

> *Industrial psychologists'* studies of various work methods and conditions, and interpersonal relations
>
> *Industrial sociologists'* research on group dynamics and the social organization of work, and interpersonal relations
>
> *Clinical psychologists' or psychiatrists'* insights gained while helping people solve troubles in which tired feelings loomed large

These specialists in human nature have found that the inner self has much to do with making people feel tired. They

"I JUST DON'T KNOW HOW TO HANDLE THESE KIDS..... WHAT SHALL I DO?"

From the booklet "Needlepoint." Courtesy The Connecticut Mutual Life Insurance Co.

Part of the New View. Distressing situations which a person feels helpless to do anything about are a potent cause of tired feelings can now tell us a great deal about the role that one's motives, attitudes, and personal difficulties play, both in starting and in increasing the tired feelings that plague normal people. The last three chartoons in this chapter illustrate some of the findings from this stream; a careful study of these chartoons will widen your view of tired feelings.

(This work curve shows how Dr. Robert S. Woodworth performed at this trying day-long task at age 29.)

Data from Dr. Edward L. Thorndike

No "fatigue slump" in this close inspection work (He was strongly motivated to do his best all through the day; he took only a total of 9 minutes time out during the 8 hours)

This stream has been especially fruitful in its findings about the tired feelings of white-collar and blue-collar workers who do only light manual work. The new view comes mostly from the discoveries in this stream.

We will report in nontechnical words some of the practical applications of these findings, as we see them. Although we

may have bad news to report in some places, by and large
the remainder of the book can be read through rose-colored
glasses. It should be rosy news, for instance, that the white-
collar worker does have a right to feel tired. That is the topic
of the next chapter.

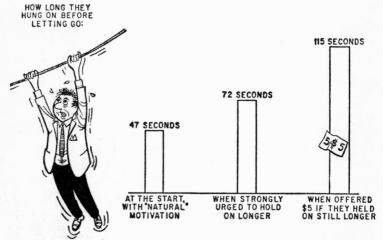

HOW LONG THEY
HUNG ON BEFORE
LETTING GO:

115 SECONDS

72 SECONDS

47 SECONDS

AT THE START,   WHEN STRONGLY   WHEN OFFERED
WITH "NATURAL"   URGED TO HOLD $5 IF THEY HELD
MOTIVATION   ON LONGER   ON STILL LONGER

Data from Dr. Robert S. Schwab

Do people tire out—or give up? (These didn't tire [or give up] as
quickly when their motivation was increased)

(In some instances you may want to read the original research. The bibliography at the end of the book lists much of
the research on which this book is based. When a scientist is
mentioned by name in the text, or under a chartoon, in most
instances you will find his supporting research listed in the
bibliography.)

CHAPTER 2

The right to feel tired

1. What Dr. Thorndike's survey showed

"Do you get tired easily?"

The U.S. Air Force wanted to know how many men tired easily in civilian life, because tiring easily is one reason aviators are grounded for "combat fatigue." The Air Force asked Dr. Robert L. Thorndike (son of the Thorndike mentioned on the chartoon of close inspection work) to find this out, as part of a survey of men's feelings of healthiness.

When white-collar men answered this question face-to-face, 10 per cent admitted that they tired easily. But twice as many confessed tiring easily when they could answer on a secret ballot which would not reveal their identity.

Why did so many of the white-collar men not want to admit publicly that they tired easily? One good guess is that

11

they didn't think they had an honest reason for feeling tired.

It was different with the Negro men who did mostly heavy manual work. About 16 per cent of these said they tired easily, and the percentage was the same whether publicly admitted or privately confessed on the secret ballot.

These findings are confirmed by experience. People who do really heavy work seldom complain as much about tired feelings as people who do light work. And those who do heavy work see no reason why they should try to conceal their tired feelings.

But most people have the belief that sedentary work should not be tiring. Pencil-pushing, paper-sorting, or talking with customers does not require much muscular exertion. So the white-collar person is likely to feel somewhat ashamed of feeling tired. Perhaps he imagines it makes him appear as a weakling.

2. The white-collar person's right to feel tired

The white-collar person should not be ashamed of tiring out. The evidence is overwhelming that a "soft job" in an office or store can be definitely tiring.

The "softest" job of all—that of executive—may be the most tiring of all. Dr. Elliott Jacques, after spending several years in the study of one manufacturing firm, reported to the congress of The Royal Society for the Promotion of Health that the demands that were made upon the executives left them especially vulnerable to tired feelings.

Such "soft jobs" often produce the most insidious kind of tiredness, because it seems unaccountable and the person worries about it. It can easily be accounted for, however, once one learns something about the inside workings of the human body and how different experiences can throw them out of balance. Stresses similar to those that bring on "combat fatigue" occur daily in white-collar jobs. Civilians are usually surprised when they learn that "combat fatigue" is not due to overwork, deprivations, or the gore of combat. Authorities such as Dr. Abram Kardiner find that it is due almost entirely to emotional stresses and the attitudes the

From booklet "The Merry-Go-Round." Courtesy The Connecticut Mutual Life Insurance Co.

A right to be tired. Work held in low esteem is hard on the person's inner self and is likely to be tiring, even though the work is light

person takes toward these stresses. "Combat fatigue" is the result of the person's private reactions to situations which distress him in one way or another. Some people get ulcers, some high blood pressure, others come down with tired feelings, all depending upon the individual's style, or perhaps habit, of reacting to distressing events. That is why the expression "combat fatigue" has to be put in quotation marks nowadays. The condition is very real—not imaginary—and the person may feel so worn out that he is utterly unable to work. But the fighting as such has practically nothing to do with it in most instances.

From booklet "The Merry-Go-Round." Courtesy The Connecticut Mutual Life Insurance Co.

A right to feel tired. Rivalry and envy often cause personality clashes which bring on tired feelings

People in the rat race of white-collar work have stresses which are similar to those of, say, the bomber pilot in combat. The desk worker, as well as the combat pilot, has to be vigilant and concentrate when conditions around him may be distracting. He has to guard against making errors, has to make many spur-of-the-moment decisions and be responsible for their consequences. He has to work against time pressure occasionally, and often has to do tasks he would rather not do.

In addition, stress often bears down on the white-collar worker from exasperating demands of his boss, and from having to compete with ambitious rivals for promotion. There are discouraging frustrations which can take the heart out of him. And many times he has to be nice to irritating fellow workers, or unreasonable customers, when he feels like slamming the door in their faces.

Throw into that stew a dash of boredom for workers on light routine jobs that lack variety, or who strongly wish they were in different work, or who feel pushed around because they are not permitted to plan the details of their work for themselves. There are reasons galore for white-collar workers developing their own particular variety of "combat fatigue."

3. Situations likely to bring on tired feelings

The things that may give one a right to feel tired are so numerous it is difficult to remember them. We will accordingly group them into a few classes which can be easily kept in mind, and which will also give a sharper picture of the new view.

- A. *Overwork* which runs down one's energy supply (Very rare in ordinary life)
- B. *Diseases* which exhaust, as in chronic infections, or interfere with, as in diabetes, the use of one's energy
- C. *Bodily conditions* which exhaust or interfere with the use of energy, as in:
    Sedentary living (Very common)
    Vitamin shortages (Rare)
    Allergies

    Old age
    Overweight
    High altitudes
    Hot work places
  D. *Personality clashes,* off the job as well as on the job,
     which threaten the inner self and produce reactions that
     disrupt the use of energy (Very common)
  E. *Restrictive situations,* off the job as well as in one's work,
     which threaten the inner self and thereby produce at-
     titudes that make it difficult to use one's energy (Very
     common)

The old view of tired feelings centered on the first three
of those groups, overlooking the last two.

The new view includes all five classes, but gives great
emphasis to the last two—personality clashes, or restrictive
situations which threaten the inner self.

It is not an exaggeration to say that in our modern world
sedentary living, personality clashes, and restrictive situations cause tired feelings ten times as often as overwork
and disease do. Even when the tired feelings are associated
with overwork, it is often not because the exertion has run
down energy, but because the atttiudes that were aroused
in the person by clashes and restrictions while doing the
work have made it seem so. And the tired feelings which
spring from sedentary living, clashes, and restrictive situations are almost always most puzzling and distressing to the
person who has them.

At the 149th annual meeting of the Medical Society of the
State of New York, Dr. Edward A. Burkhardt, of Cornell University Medical College, said: "The many and varied demands placed on us in our present-day civilization lead to the
conclusion that tired feelings are truly an inalienable right of
every American."

Data from Dr. Nancy C. Morse

A right to feel tired in a large insurance office

4. When medical tests are called for

Although only a small share of tired feelings are caused by disease, most (but not all) diseases can cause them. When a person is ill he often expects to feel tired. Not simply sick, but sick and tired.

How can you tell whether your tired feelings mean you should hurry to your family physician, or clinic, for a going-over? Here are two ways.

> Tired feelings usually come and go throughout the day when they are not related to some bodily disturbance. If they hang on for a few days, better have a physician investigate.
>
> Tired feelings usually fade away after rest. If they linger on after what should be adequate rest, it is wise to find out why.

What are medical tests likely to show? We can get an idea from what was found with 300 people who went to the Lahey Clinic, in Boston, because they had "chronic fatigue," weakness, or weak spells which hung on regardless of rest and which they could not account for. The examinations by Dr. Frank N. Allan revealed some bodily disease in only one out of four of these tired persons. The bodily causes found are listed below; many other disease conditions bring on tired feelings, but were not present in these particular cases.

Hidden infections (lungs, air passages, urinary system)	12 people
Heart disease	8
Diabetes	8
Narcolepsy	8
Anemia (severe)	5
Thyroid disorder	4
Myasthenia gravis	4
Epilepsy	3
Syphilis	1
Brain tumor	1
Vitamin shortage	1
Lung tumor	1
Unclassified fever	1
Hodgkin's disease	1
Total	58 out of 300 people

What made the other three out of four feel so lacking in energy all the time? Nothing could be found in their bodies to account for the chronic tiredness. That does not mean, however, that their tired feelings were imaginary. There are lots of other good reasons for feeling tired.

These 300 went to the clinic solely because they were chronically tired. Dr. Henry P. Laughlin, of George Washington University School of Medicine, made a survey among internists to find out how large a share of their patients sought medical help primarily because of tiredness. The internists estimated that feeling tired was the primary complaint in about one third of their patients.

From the booklet "Needlepoint." Courtesy The Connecticut Mutual Life Insurance Co.

A right to feel tired. Although housework uses little energy, it may bring on tired feelings in the woman who looks upon it as restrictive

But many who go to an internist to find out what is wrong have tiredness as a secondary symptom. They may complain about "not feeling right in the stomach," but on talking with them the physician finds they are also pestered by tiredness.

Dr. Geoffrey E. Ffrench has reported on 1170 consecutive patients who were referred to him for diagnosis. These were "run of the mill" cases that the general practitioners had difficulty diagnosing, not people referred primarily because of chronic tiredness, as were those studied by Dr. Allan.

Dr. Ffrench found that 105 of these people complained of tiredness, lassitude, or exhaustion. Here are the diagnoses of the condition that probably caused the tired feelings in these cases.

Alcoholic gastritis	1 person
Anemia	6
Aneurysm of aorta	1
Anxiety tensions	26
Cancer of colon	2
Cancer of lung	2
Cerebrovascular disease	1
Cholecystitis	2
Cirrhosis and hepatitis	9
Dental infection	1
Depression states	2
Diabetes mellitus	4
Duodenal ulcer	4
Encephalitis	1
Goiter	1
Heart disease	9
Hypertension	1
Hypoglycemia	1
Hypothyroidism	3
Ileitis	1
Influenza	2
Labyrinthitis	1
Leukemia	1
Malaria	1
Infectious mononucleosis	6
Nephritis	2
Obesity	2
Overwork	2
Pneumonia	1
Pregnancy	2
Pyrexia of unknown origin	1
Sinusitis	1
Thyrotoxicosis	5
Total	105 out of 1170 people

It is worth noting that not every one of these people who had one of those disorders felt tired enough to complain about it. In the entire group of 1170, for instance, there were 166 who had heart disease of some sort, but only 9 of these complained about being tired. This is the way the more frequent diagnoses lined up in this respect:

Hypothyroidism	50%	of those who had it complained about feeling tired
Anemia	42	
Liver disease	39	
Infectious mononucleosis	37	
Hyperthyroidism	35	
Anxiety tensions	25	
Duodenal ulcer	18	
Diabetes mellitus	14	
Heart disease	5	

It is of special interest to us in this book that only two of the people who complained of tiredness could be diagnosed as being that way because of overwork. The tired person may feel that he is overworking, simply because in his condition any work seems difficult.

It is also important that 26 of the people who complained about feeling tired were diagnosed as cases of anxiety tension—the largest single group among the tired cases. But there were 78 others of the people diagnosed as suffering from anxiety tension who had not complained about tiredness.

The total number of people having a chronic or acute anxiety state (104) was second only to those with heart disease (166). Dr. Ffrench believes that the large number of anxiety patients was in part due to the fact that most of the people referred for diagnosis came from the suburbs around a large city. They were likely to be subjected to the stresses—personality clashes and restrictiveness—of competitive business life and also to the problems associated with commuting to work.

What do such findings mean to you? A great deal. If you have persisting tiredness that is not clearly due to heavy physical work, the first step is to have a thorough examination to track down possible bodily causes. If your family physician cannot find a physical cause, ask him to refer you to a clinic or internist especially qualified to run down puzzling cases. Maybe nothing wrong with your body will be discovered! That is what is most likely to happen. But, again, it may not only solve your tiredness but also save your life, as when the steady tiredness is the result of slow internal bleeding.

The heart and soul of the new view is that threats to the inner self bring on most of the tired feelings in our modern world. As this book unfolds, we will delve more deeply into these threats which we have grouped as personality clashes or restricting situations.

At this point, and before reading the next chapter, it will be rewarding to thumb the remaining pages and look at the drawings from the booklets of the Human Relations Program of The Connecticut Mutual Life Insurance Co. These drawings, by Rama Braggiotti, depict familiar situations in which somebody's inner self, or private world, is threatened. Study of these situations now will help you grasp the meaning and significance of threats to the inner self.

CHAPTER 3

Allergies that brought on tired feelings

---

1. The farmer who was worn out by an allergy

Usually a combination of factors is to blame for tired feelings. It will be easier to understand the factors, however, if we take them up one at a time. So for our first examples we will use fairly uncomplicated instances where one factor was obviously the culprit.

Allergy tiredness is a good one to begin with because the cause-and-effect relationship is dramatically demonstrated—remove the substance to which the person is allergic, and presto! the tiredness disappears. Also, allergy tiredness is much more common than most people realize, and can be disabling. The lassitude of so-called spring fever, for instance, is probably merely an allergic manifestation of some people to the pollens that bloom in the spring.

The case of Roscoe R., a young farmer, is one of several

23

reported by Dr. Theron G. Randolph. Roscoe R. was forced to sell his farm because he was allergic to something in the barn or fields, it seemed. His nose had an allergic stuffiness, and became more so as he continued on the farm. He also developed tired feelings which steadily became worse until he "felt too weak to work." So he sold the farm and moved to the city.

Moving away from the farm did not end his tired feelings. The stuffiness was somewhat better, but the tired feelings still kept him from working. Maybe it was something other than barn dust to which he was allergic. Dr. Randolph searched for other causes, and in due course the search narrowed to what the ex-farmer ate.

One by one his foods were checked, by simply with-drawing one from his diet for a while to see if he felt less tired when he avoided it.

Then they came to the wheat products. Two days after he had gone without eating any of these, he began to feel better. After a week without wheat he was working for the first time in four months, 10 to 12 hours a day. The other discomforts due to his allergy also cleared up.

As a further check to be sure wheat was the culprit, he started eating wheat products again. Within three days he was stuffed up and tired!

So long as he ate only a little wheat every second or third day, he was feeling fit and able to work without excessive tiredness. And he had always loved bread—8 to 10 slices a day—and an equal number of cookies. When he was faced with the choice of giving up his favorite foods or having his tired feelings, he made the same choice you probably would have.

2. *Things worth knowing about allergy tiredness*

Dr. Charles H. Blackley, a very bald-headed physician in England, was the first person to discover that allergies could bring on tired feelings. In his time little was known about either allergies or tired feelings. He was inquisitive and experimented on himself for twenty years before he published his observations.

He noted that when he intentionally inhaled the pollen dust from flowers his nose became stuffy a few minutes later and he had difficulty breathing. About five hours after sniffing the pollen he began to feel tired and weary all over. That tiredness lasted a couple of days. Could it have been caused by the flower pollen? he wondered. So he tried sniffing some pollen again, and, sure enough, in about five hours he was as tired as before.

It seemed mysterious, but now it is known that allergies are something to reckon with in more ways than one. An allergy is simply an unusual susceptibility to some substance; most people may not be affected by the substance, but to a few it acts almost as a poison.

Almost anything can cause an allergic reaction in some persons. Many of the materials used in manufacturing bring on allergic reactions in one person or another. Employers are familiar with this in the skin rashes that are caused in some workers. They are not as familiar, however, with the possibility of tired feelings coming from this source. Imagine what Roscoe R.'s plight would have been if he had worked in a bakery!

The products of one's own body may touch off an allergic reaction at times. In hard muscular work, as an example, histamine is produced by the muscles themselves. This is a potent allergy-producing substance, and a few people are honestly allergic to muscular work. Men have been released from military service because of this allergy.

Susceptibility to allergies is usually shown by sneezing, skin rash or itching, watering eyes, nasal drip, and stuffiness, sometimes by headaches or stomach upsets. And sometimes by otherwise unexplainable tiredness.

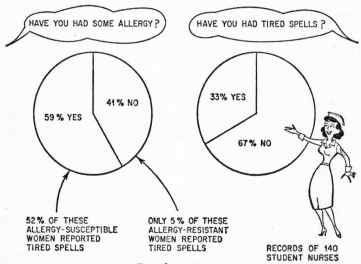

Data from Drs. T. G. Randolph and R. A. Hettig

The young women who had allergies in their past were much more likely to have had puzzling spells of tired feelings that resting did not relieve

Tired feelings associated with allergies may be much more widespread than is ordinarily realized. The chartoon shows, in the circle on the right, that one-third of a group of healthy young women had been bothered by unexplained tired spells. The circle on the left shows how these tired spells had occurred in ten times as many who had histories of allergy in their past.

Tired feelings due to allergies also occur in children, even infants. Dr. Frederic Speer has made special studies of this, and reported many instances of children in predicaments similar to Roscoe R.'s. He has found that in children this tiredness is often accompanied by tension or irritability so that the child is not only tired but also jittery.

The tiredness is probably due, in both children and adults, to their body chemistry being changed temporarily by something they breathe, or touch, or eat. The autonomic nervous system is especially affected.

3. Tracking it down

Sometimes it is easy to track down the cause of an allergic reaction—poison ivy, for instance. But it is usually tricky business and almost always requires a specialist to do the job properly. Skin tests can be used to find out if the person is unusually susceptible to a large number of common allergy-causing substances. But in most instances it also requires patient detective work and trial-and-error testing to track down the culprit. This is especially so when some foodstuff is responsible and special test diets have to be used. Consider the person who is sensitive to wheat as an illustration. Such a person could avoid bread, cakes, and pies and still suffer from his allergy because of the small amount of flour used to thicken gravies and soups. It takes ingenuity, and time.

One thing that adds to the difficulty of tracking down the offender is that the tired feeling does not always come on the instant the allergic substance is touched, or breathed, or eaten. Remember that Dr. Blackley was not overcome by tiredness until five hours after exposing himself to the substance. Thus the person may begin to feel tired after eating his noon meal, although the tiredness is due to something he had for breakfast. This is another reason for having an expert who understands the tricks of allergies to track down the offender.

Once the offender is spotted, does that mean that it has to be avoided the rest of one's life? Not always, but sometimes that is the simplest way. An electrician, for instance, was found to be allergic to one variety of soldering flux. By merely using a different formula flux he was freed of his tiredness in a few days.

It is often possible for the specialist to plan a regimen that will enable the person to increase his tolerance to the offending substance. That was done for Roscoe R. so that he could eat a slice or two of bread every other day without bad results.

It should also be noted that an allergy can play a secondary role in tiredness, even when it does not cause it directly. A person is inclined to be cranky and touchy when bothered by an allergy. This gives him temporarily a disposition which gets him involved in clashes with others, or which makes things seem restrictive to him.

And this is the point at which it is appropriate to get acquainted with what personality clashes can do.

CHAPTER 4

Personality clashes that make people tired

1. The woman who was worn out by a personality clash

People—other people, of course—are a prevalent cause of tired feelings. Usually it is only moderate tiredness they cause, but in some instances it can be of knock-out proportions.

Eunice H. was one knocked out by a clash. She had difficulty getting along with her mother, who lived with her. The mother was too aggressive to suit Eunice; moreover, the mother's conversation was mostly complaining. At the breakfast table, for instance, Eunice would often become upset by her mother's complaints about the world in general. Eunice yearned then to shout "Shut up!" or to leave the table. But she held her hostility in check and remained politely at the table trying not to listen.

Some time after breakfast Eunice would suddenly be overwhelmed by extreme tired feelings and want to go back to bed to rest. Some days she continued to feel so tired that she spent most of the hours on her bed.

She discovered that if she went for a walk with her dog as soon as the tiredness overtook her, she could "walk it off," or master it. But on most days she felt too tired to take that beneficial walk. (We'll come back to this aspect several times.)

2. Hostile impulses cause the trouble

Dr. Harley C. Shands, who reported Eunice's plight, has found that in such personality clashes the hostile impulses which are held back—such as *not* saying "Shut up!"—give rise to anxiety. The sudden onset of the tiredness is due to an anxiety attack over the "murderous" or unsocial impulses touched off by the clash.

Accordingly, merely being irritated by someone may not make much trouble. The tiredness is more likely to come from being upset by the hostile impulses we feel toward the other person. In view of this, we would expect those who want to "do the right thing," or to "behave decently," to be more susceptible to tired feelings from personality clashes than those who "don't give a damn."

3. How clashes sneak up on people

Clashes can occur without bystanders noticing them. And Jane may clash with Rose without being aware she is rubbing Rose the wrong way. Eunice's mother, for instance, was blissfully unaware of the distressing effect she had on her daughter. This has unfortunate aspects; for example, bosses cannot see that they, the bosses, have clashed and put the whole force in low gear.

The person most affected may not be aware that he has been in a clash, because he does not have a close acquaintance with his own inner self which has suffered in the collision. He just feels, and often suddenly, tired all over, and

From the booklet "Needlepoint." Courtesy The Connecticut Mutual Life Insurance Co.

Feeling overshadowed by a significant person in your life often gives rise to a personality clash that results in tired feelings

never thinks to look back for a clash that may have caused it. What you don't know can tire you!

There can be a collision of personalities without a noisy argument, or weeping, or fighting. In fact, if there were some such outward action the impact might be less, as was the case with Eunice H. when she could pull herself together and "walk it off." More about this shortly.

Two people need to be only slightly out of harmony to bring out tired feelings in one, or perhaps both, of the people involved. It depends largely upon their inner attitudes. The person who has a sensitive inner self can be bowled over by a tiny clash, reacting to a pinprick as if it were a sword thrust.

Here are illustrations of situations which frequently—but not always—seem to threaten a sensitive inner self and touch off tired feelings:

Being ignored or neglected	Being criticized or disparaged
Being overshadowed	Being bossed or "picked on"
Being interrupted or distracted	Being nagged or "preached at"
Being jealous of the other person	Being discriminated against
Simply disliking the person	Being bored by the other person

Wanting to be alone

4. The clashes that cause the most trouble

It is important to note that the worst clashes for tired feelings are those we have *with a person who is significant to us* in some way. We can be annoyed by a stranger at the bus terminal and suffer only brief irritation at "the old fool." There will probably be no tired feelings from such a collision, unless someone's inner self wants to be popular with the entire world.

But when the clash is with a relative, sweetheart, boss, or person whose friendliness you cherish, you are then dealing with a person who is significant to you. Minor friction with such a person is much more likely to bring on a bad spell of tiredness than would a heated argument with a traffic cop in a strange city.

The importance of significant persons is illustrated in the chartoon. This deals with hostility rather than with tired feelings directly, but in either case the tendency is much the same—the more significant the person is to you, the harder a clash with him hits you.

In the same experiment that gave these results it was also found (not charted) that when the criticized person had a chance to talk back to the tormentor, there was much less drop in friendliness. "Talking it out" seems to work somewhat the same as "walking it off" did for Eunice H.

Data from Drs. J. W. Thibaut and J. Coules

People being as they are, we inevitably bump into clashing personalities, whether we ourselves are the touchy kind or not. But the touchier we happen to be, the more tired feelings we can expect from these collisions or irritations.

In later chapters we will take up some pointers for handling ourselves in such situations. But next we should begin to think about restrictive situations which are similar to clashes in that they often sneak up on people, as well as being a prevalent cause of tired feelings.

CHAPTER 5

Restrictive situations that touch off tiredness

1. The executive who was worn out

Fred N. was a career man in government service. He had been ambitious, but not overly so, and had been more successful than most in his rise up the echelons.

At age forty, however, he began to slip in his work, largely, he thought at first, because he felt so tired. Mornings were the worst. He felt somewhat less tired as the day wore on. But even so, his leaden legs could barely carry him home and he was too tired to do anything evenings. "I have no energy left," he explained it.

Dr. Henry P. Laughlin found that a restrictive situation was the cause of Fred's plight. The restrictions of red tape

34

and standard procedures did not bother him, although many people do react to them as restrictive. Fred had long taken red tape and official procedures for granted; he even felt some security from knowing his way around the mysteries of official channels.

But here he was, turned forty, and it began to dawn on his inner self that he had landed in a nice dignified job that was a dead end. His chance of fulfilling his ambition for further promotions was restricted, and there was nothing he could do to alter the system. More than that, he did not enjoy his present job, disliked it, in fact, and that, too, was restrictive. So he inevitably began to feel tired and to hope that something might happen to open a new way to get ahead; he felt too tired to try to do anything about it himself.

Thanks to outside help, Fred was able to get better acquainted with his inner self and pull himself together. He located a different job in which he was genuinely interested, and which would also lead somewhere. His tired feelings dropped as he got away from the restrictive situation and took a more realistic attitude toward himself and the world in which he had to live and work.

2. Things worth knowing about restrictive situations

We expect military life to be restrictive. That is one reason many leave it, despite the steady work and other advantages. This unavoidable restrictiveness is also regarded as a factor that makes some men more susceptible to "combat fatigue"—their combat with restrictiveness.

But the military does not have a monopoly on restrictiveness. An amazing number of things in our modern world can be restrictive, more so for some people than for others, depending upon the individual's abilities, interests, ambitions, and hopes. Situations which a person looks upon as restrictive are regarded as one of the most potent causes of his tired feelings, and also as one of the most frequent causes.

Sometimes the restrictive situations are doubly potent because they involve personality clashes as well. An example is friction with the boss who is the key man in work assignments and promotions. The same can be said for restrictive home or school situations, because there are significant persons included in the situation.

Because of their significance, we will have more examples and discussions of restrictive situations and what to do about them later in the book. At this point we need a general view of what a restrictive situation is, and this can be given by listing situations which people often feel are cramping them, putting them in strait jackets, shoving them around, chaining them to their jobs, or frustrating them, as it is variously expressed. As you scan these lists, you will be impressed with the number of them you have faced in your own work, home life, even in recreation.

RESTRICTIVE SITUATIONS

In general:	*On the job:*
Anything one wants to change, but can't	Having work inspected
Having to wait	Working faster, or slower, than one prefers
Financial loss, or close straits	Not being free to come and go at will
Having to fill in forms, make reports	Cramped quarters
Not safe to express honest opinions	Little chance to be original
Having to compromise, or go against one's principles	Slow advancement

RESTRICTIVE SITUATIONS

In general:

Working for others rather than for oneself

Inability to buy what one would like to

Being held to a timetable, or schedule

Inability to control the actions of someone else

Being discriminated against for any reason

Having to do anything that does not interest one

Having to do something in which one fears one may fail

Laws, rules, regulations, prohibitions

Being with disliked people

Having too little to do—killing time

Having too much to do—under pressure

On the job:

Work low in public esteem

Too much sameness, not enough variety

Doing work planned by someone else

Doing repetitive work that is too easy

Being ordered around

Competing for promotions

Not being allowed to move around, or to talk

Uncomfortable surroundings

Poor tools, materials

Not being able to use full talents

Being isolated from others

In the person:

Poor vision, or poor hearing

Disease, or weakness, which prevents a person from doing what he wants to

More ambition than ability

"Touchy" feelings

Scant ability for the job

Inability to eat what one would like to

Lack of self-confidence

Love and other personal problems

3. *Why some people take it harder than others*

Each of those situations has proven restrictive enough to plunge some persons into bad cases of tired feelings. But for others a similar situation may not appear restricting —"just don't mind it, one way or the other." Such individual differences have led some behavioral scientists to say: "Tell me what makes you feel tired, and I'll tell you the kind of person you are."

There are two important points which stem from this. One is that the mere existence of the situation, such as poor tools, may not be felt as restrictive by everybody who is confronted with it. The person has to feel it as restrictive, or frustrating. That is why some scientists prefer to speak of *felt restrictions*.

The other point is that the affected individual quite often is not clearly aware what is restrictive to him about a situation. This is because people have deep-lying hopes or motives—an inner self—with which they are not acquainted. When one of those deep motives is restricted, he just becomes aware of feeling tired, and can't point to the motive or what exactly restricts it—another instance that what we don't know can make us tired. In view of this, the phrase "felt restriction" is not quite complete; "reacted to as restrictive" describes it better.

We will have to talk many times about restrictiveness as we make progress toward answers to the double-barreled question. Each time we will mean *reacted to as restrictive*.

Feeling tired is not the only way people react to such restrictive situations. Other ways will be briefly discussed in the chapter on "The Distinctive Mark of Tired Feelings."

From the booklet "The Merry-Go-Round." Courtesy
The Connecticut Mutual Life Insurance Co.

**Waiting is often reacted to as being restrictive, and may bring on tired
feelings without any visible work having been done**

4. The physician who had to take pep pills

The most handicapping, or chronic, tired feelings generally
arise from a combination of conditions, as the next two
stories illustrate.

Isaac G. was a brilliant young physician and micro-
biologist who moved upward from a university laboratory
to take charge of research for a large drug firm. The new
job had great prestige and provided Isaac with almost limit-
less facilities, but he soon found it more restricting than the
academic freedom he had known. He felt restricted by all
the people he had to deal with, subordinates as well as
higher ups. It was restricting to have to "grind, grind, at an

ever faster pace," as he phrased it. The restrictiveness that upset him most was due to the things he had to do to help the sale of new drugs and which conflicted with his code of conduct as a pure scientist.

After a year on the new job Isaac was so pestered by tired feelings that he began to take pep pills. Three years later, his immediate superior, whom he had admired and found helpful, was replaced. Now Isaac had to work with a critical, exacting, supercilious, and generally disliked man.

Personality clashes were thus added to the restrictiveness. He increased the dosage of pep pills in order to keep going. Two years of these big doses and he was in such a precarious state that he had to be hospitalized. That was when Dr. Peter H. Knapp, to whom we are indebted for the story, came in touch with Isaac and began the long course of his rehabilitation.

5. *The widow who broke her wrist*

Margaret S., a widow who was helping her son through school by working in a department store, had a temporary physical condition which seemed restricting to her inner self. Just before a vacation period she fractured her wrist, which could make anyone feel "sick and tired" for a few days.

But Margaret's tired feelings lingered on and became more handicapping. "It feels as though I've done all I can and couldn't lift my arms any more, couldn't keep on, must stop and rest," she told Dr. W. B. Spaulding.

This temporary disability was restricting her in several ways. It disrupted her vacation plans and made her financial condition precarious. She could not keep the apartment as tidy as she wished. She was apprehensive that she could not continue her son's education.

From booklet "Growing Pains." Courtesy
The Connecticut Mutual Life Insurance Co.

Look for a combination. Personality clashes and restrictive situations often occur together. In the instance pictured, all three people may end up feeling tired

To give her a new view on what she felt was restrictive, she was assured that her painful wrist would be as good as new within a short time. She was also urged to take walks and visit friends, which her employment had previously restricted her from doing. Three weeks later her tired feelings were gone, and she confessed that the forced and unplanned vacation had been enjoyable.

6. "Tropical fatigue"

This provides an interesting illustration of how the new view has modified the old view of tired feelings, and also that a combination of factors is usually the cause of feeling "all pooped out."

Ever since Europeans and Americans began to do business in the tropics, "tropical fatigue" has been a handicap and also a great deceiver. After being stationed in the tropics for a few months, executives and technicians usually begin to lose their pep. This becomes progressively worse as a rule, and after a couple years the person is too tired to do much work.

In recognition of this condition, companies and governments have the policy of bringing personnel back to the homeland for every third or fourth year, to "rest up" in a temperate climate. If the white man stays permanently in the tropics, without these refreshers, he may deteriorate in character and end up as a beachcomber or a heavy drinker and lazy individual.

The name "tropical fatigue" was given to this letdown because it was assumed there was something about the climate that wore out the white man. It is common knowledge that physical work in a hot location makes heavy physiological demands and is especially tiring. So it was natural to assume it was the heat of the tropics, or the heat combined with humidity, that got the best of people who had been used to a more temperate climate. Also, there are the fevers and internal parasites peculiar to the tropics which could run down a man's condition.

Strangely, the natives seldom complain about feeling tired. For years it was assumed that this was perhaps because their darker skin protected them from the sun, or because they were immune to the parasites which infest them. This problem was important enough that the British government set up research teams to study it on the spot. The findings of these scientists, reported in *Symposium on Fatigue*, edited by Drs. W. F. Floyd and A. T. Welford, are that the climate has little to do with it. The name "tropical fatigue," like "combat fatigue," is misleading and belongs in quotation marks.

These researchers found that what does tire out the white man in the tropics, and possibly demoralizes him, is what we are calling clashes and restrictiveness in this book. Climate and parasites apparently play a part. Clashes play a little more, and the restrictiveness of the foreign customs and traditions the biggest part.

The restrictiveness and clashes arise from the fact that the American or European is a foreigner, used to a different way of life. The natives, who are in the majority, look upon him and treat him as different; the white is a member of a minority and a marked man. It is difficult for him to win friends among the natives, and he may be afraid of them. It is easy for him to feel like an outcast.

Moreover, his diet is restricted. Many foods he likes and has been accustomed to eat are simply not available. He is homesick, so to speak, for beefsteak and apple pie.

His recreations are also restricted—no bowling, no baseball, no current magazines. Life becomes intensely monotonous and boring after the first few months. Soon he is driven to his wits' end to find ways to entertain himself. That is when the bottle and native women may attract him, and he starts on the route to becoming an outcast among both natives and whites.

Such findings indicate that something more than air conditioning and remedies for tropical diseases are needed to handle "tropical fatigue." This is why military establishments in such locations now have the latest movies and magazines flown in to them, and frozen foods they were used to at home, and visits by celebrities of all varieties from the homeland. In short, anything that will lessen the restrictive feeling when surrounded by a way of life that conflicts with many aspects of the ways one has been used to.

Why should we feel "out of energy" when we are in a restrictive situation? Or clashing with another personality?

In the next chapter we will find that we almost never are really out of energy. Following that we will learn that much does go on in the body to block the use of energy, even though we have done no visible work.

CHAPTER 6

Our amazing supply of energy

1. "Income tax tiredness"

Figuring income tax is light work. It uses only a fraction more calories of energy than merely sitting and daydreaming. Dr. Francis G. Benedict was the first to report that a single salted peanut supplies enough energy for two hours of such mental work.

Why, then, do people feel so worn out that they begin to make errors and have difficulty keeping on with the figuring? Is it "only in the mind"?

It is very much in the body, but ordinarily you can't see that it is going on in the body. Light work of this sort— even *no* work—wears people down because there is a vast amount of invisible activity going on that is not seen by the naked eye. Scientists have invented methods to study the

45

invisible activities, and with these methods have made discoveries that have greatly changed the old views of tired feelings.

"Mental fatigue" or "emotional fatigue" used to seem mysterious, like something that came from nowhere. But now they are looked upon as in fact tied in with invisible activities in the body. When these invisible activities are thrown out of balance, or are disorganized (as by the restrictiveness of figuring income taxes), the body's use of energy is disrupted. We feel tired as a consequence, and it's certainly not "all in the mind."

In view of this, "physical fatigue" and "mental fatigue" have to be considered as the tiredness twins. Almost identical twins, though not completely identical, as a later chapter will reveal. In the light of present knowledge the best way to name them would be:

> Physical fatigue is the tired feeling
> following visible activity
> Mental fatigue is the tired feeling
> following invisible activity

Now for a closer look at the first kind of activity; we will take up the other kind in the next chapter.

2. We seldom run out of energy

Everyone expects the visible activity of muscular work to make one feel tired sooner or later, and says it is "because the work uses up energy." Sometimes it does deplete the energy supply, but such instances are rare and occur mostly in connection with a disease. Humans who are in good health have an amazing supply of energy to keep them going a long time, as is shown by the tabulation "The Energy People Have for Work." White-collar work, and

How hard	Pulse rate, per min.	Breathing per min.	Calories used per min.	Work examples (Numeral shows calories per min.)		How long you can safely keep it up
Light work 1. Mild	Under 100	14 or less	1 to 4	Typing Clerical Cooking Light assembly Ironing Washing windows Driving truck	1½ 1½ 1 to 2 2 2 3 4	Indefinitely
2. Moderate	Under 120	15 or less	5 to 8	Scrubbing on knees Assembling 25-lb. parts Hand printing Shoveling 9-lb load	5 5 5 8	8 hours daily on job
Heavy work *3. OPTIMAL	Under 140	16 or less	9 to 10	Walking at 5 mph Hand riveting Blacksmithing	10 10 10	8 hours daily for a few weeks
4. Strenuous	Under 160	20 or less	11 to 12	Shoveling 14-lb. load Rowing boat at 3 mph	11 11	4 hours, two or three times a week if special training
Severe work 5. Maximal	Under 180	25 or less	13 to 15	College football Hard stair climbing	13 14	1 or 2 hours, on scattered occasions
6. Exhausting	180 and up	30 and up	16 and up	Shoveling wet snow 23-lb. load Crew rowing	18 19 to 20	Few minutes only, on rare occasions

* Work at Optimal level uses approximately half the capacity the average adult has for physical work, and should not deplete the energy of an adult who is in good condition.
(Adapted from experiments by Dr. J. Gordon Wells and Dr. Bruno Balke at the U.S. Air Force School of Aviation Medicine)

most blue-collar work, scarcely scratch the surface of one's energy supply. When we feel completely exhausted, it is almost never because we have run out of energy.

The energy that muscles use most easily, and by preference, comes from carbohydrates which are stored in the body. If the carbohydrate supply happens to be used up, which is rarely, then the fat stored in the body is converted into a form that the muscles can use almost as well as they do the original carbohydrate supply.

How long could you keep on doing fairly heavy work if you did not eat to replenish the carbohydrate supply? After five or six hours you might be hungry as a bear, and perhaps feel tuckered out. But you would scarcely have used the thin top layer of that energy source.

Dr. David B. Dill reports, for example, that experiments at the Harvard Fatigue Laboratory showed that a man had to keep at moderate work for nearly 24 hours *without food* before he used up his carbohydrate energy reserves. And when the carbohydrate reserves were used up he still had energy to draw on from his body fat. (But that is no argument for having a lot of surplus fat wrapped around one's carcass.)

Only people who have regular work that comes under the classification of Strenuous, Maximal, or Exhausting in the tabulation need worry about exhausting their energy supplies. Even in those cases the energy is promptly restored by the usual three square meals a day.

There have been periods and places, however, where the energy spent in work was greater than the energy supplied by the food—during the potato famine in Ireland, for instance, and among the Ruhr miners in World War I.

After surgery, or severe illness, there may also be a shortage. Those who undergo such experiences may need new energy supplies desperately but be too tired, or too weak, to eat.

But probably not one person in a thousand who reads this book does work that is hard enough and continued long enough to make more than a dent in his energy supply.

3. How our use of energy is disrupted

What usually has happened when we say we feel tired following muscular work is that conditions in the body have been thrown out of balance for the time being so that the *use* of the body's store of energy is disrupted. This is an important modern conception to keep clearly in mind. We have energy enough and almost never need "quick-energy foods"—unless we want to put on weight. The practical problem is not restoring energy, but restoring the balance between the various bodily processes.

The body is a marvelously intricate and balanced machine. Almost every function is related to, or dependent upon, other functions. The processes are continually varying this way or that so that they work together in a balance that will keep the person going under the existing conditions. For one illustration we will consider the change in balance due to the oxygen shortage which occurs as the visible activity is continued. It is quite a story.

Muscles can work hard—up to a point—without needing fresh oxygen. That point is reached fairly soon with many people. After climbing a few steps, for example, a sedentary person is tuckered out because the blood of sedentary people has "become lazy" and does not carry as much oxygen as it could.

The bodily processes are so interrelated that as soon as extra oxygen is needed in one muscle, the processes shift their usual balance and oxygen is rushed where it will do the most good—special delivery. Here are some of the shifts that are made to accomplish this special delivery.

> Blood vessels in the oxygen-short muscle enlarge and a larger share of blood can reach the muscle
>
> The heart speeds up, increasing the flow of blood to all muscles
>
> Breathing becomes deeper, enabling the blood to pick up more oxygen in the lungs

The heart or pulse rate is thus a useful over-all indicator of the "heaviness" of work, and also tells whether the person has worked beyond the safe limit. It also indicates roughly how much the bodily processes in general have been thrown out of balance while adjusting to the load of visible work.

The chartoon shows how this general balance was upset

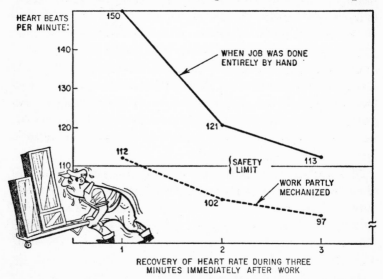

Data from Dr. Lucien Brouha

Using machines to do some of the lifting and hammering brought the work stress down to safe limits

by strenuous work. From the lower curve on the chartoon we can see that there was much less disruption when machines were used to do some of the heavier part of the work. (More about heart-rate recovery when we get to Chapter 10.)

4. *The steady state*

There are many other less spectacular changes when a person engages in visible activity. These changes represent shifts in the *steady state,* as Dr. Walter B. Cannon named it in 1926, that is maintained by the body.

When this steady state is disrupted, it is a signal to "call out the militia" to restore law and order—deeper breathing and more rapid heart rate are examples. Any shift from the usual balance thus touches off changes of various processes so the customary steady state can be regained and there will be no undue stress or strain on any of the processes—so you "purr along smoothly" again, in a steady state.

Feeling tired appears to be one of the changes that help us regain the steady state. This feeling leads one to ease up the visible activity, giving nature a chance to restore the balance without outside interference. A chance to tune the engine, we might say, without having some amateurs interfere with the work.

What effects do personality clashes and restrictive situations have upon the steady state? They can have more disrupting effects than does hard work without food, as the following chapter describes.

CHAPTER 7

How the inner self affects the use of energy

1. Glands and nerves that speed or slow us

Hard physical work uses up lots of calories of energy.

Mental work, personality clashes, and restrictive situations use only a few calories—not many more than if we were sleeping. Why, then, do we feel "all out of energy"?

The answer seems to be that when a clash or restrictive situation threatens one's inner self the steady state is thrown out of balance so that the use of energy is disrupted. There are two systems of organs in the body that have key parts in changing the balance in one direction or the other, and which are also especially sensitive to clashes and restrictions:

52

The autonomic parts of the nervous system
The ductless, or endocrine glands

The ductless glands—especially the pituitary, thyroid, adrenal—and the autonomic parts of the nervous system have parallel functions in regulating the other internal organs and processes. They can speed up, or slow down, almost every process in the body. The changes they bring about are almost never seen or felt directly.

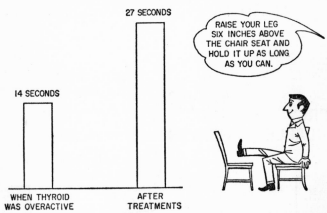

Data from Dr. Muriel H. Stern

More "sustained strength" after overactive thyroid glands had been calmed down

When the right arm is worked hard, for instance, it is the autonomic nerves that dilate the arteries in that arm, allowing more blood to flow to the oxygen-hungry muscles.

Most of the time these glands and autonomics, as we will refer to them, work as a cooperative team. They can shift the body functions so a person feels chock-full of energy, or—the next moment!—make him feel entirely at a loss for the energy to keep going at his work, regardless of whether he has done any work to use his energy.

The balance of these glands and autonomics is most likely to be upset by emotions and attitudes—clashes and restrictive situations, for example.

Their balance may also be upset by some physical disease. Dr. James Kemble has gathered evidence, for instance, which indicates strongly that Napoleon developed a pituitary ailment at about age 40. Before that age, Napoleon scarcely knew what it was to feel tired. But when this gland began to fail him, he was overtaken by tiredness and spells of inactivity which steadily became worse. The pituitary, located

HOW TIRED FEELINGS

A Steady State
"Feel energetic"

The energy available and the bodily processes are in balance. Energy is not used up by visible work (left side), and use of energy is not disrupted by clashes or restrictions which would affect the actions of nerves and glands (right side)

Upset by visible activity
"Feel tired"

Muscular work lowers the energy available and thus upsets the steady state. Usually the balance is promptly restored by rest while oxygen and blood sugar are making fresh energy available. Disease may make energy available low

(Much more complicated than in this summary)

at the bottom of the brain, is the smallest of the ductless glands in size, but the biggest in influence on the other glands.

Visible and invisible activities are always mingled together, in varying proportions. The diagram "How Tired Feelings Originate" gives the gist of how these upset the steady state. It should be studied closely. In the next sections we will give typical findings that illustrate the role of the autonomics, as shown by the pupil of the eye, and of the part played by the glands, as shown by a team of athletes and their coach.

ORIGINATE A schematic diagram

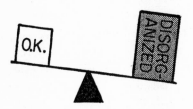 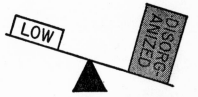

Upset by invisible activity "Feel tired"	*Visible and invisible combined* "Feel worn-out"
Work not heavy enough to deplete energy, but the steady state is upset by glands and nerves which have been disorganized by clashes and reactions to restrictiveness, or by disease. Recuperation slow because memory of clashes and restrictions lingers on	The steady state is upset by both energy depletion and disruption of glands and nerves. The clashes and restrictions involved tend to make rest or sleep poor and interfere with restoring the steady state. The most severe and long-lasting disorganization

2. What the pupil of the eye tells

Dr. Otto Lowenstein studied the pupil of the eye to learn about the workings of the autonomics in relation to tired feelings. The pupil provides an unusual opportunity because it can be observed from outside the body, and its size is controlled by opposed sections of the autonomics, thus:

Section	Its general function	What it does to the pupil
Sympathetic	Mobilizes energy: "feel energetic"	Makes it larger
Parasympathetic	Conserves energy: "feel tired"	Makes it smaller

The pupil, like every organ and involuntary muscle, is connected with both sections of the autonomics, which are the oldest and most primitive parts of the nervous system. Fibers from the sympathetic sections fan out from roughly the middle half of the length of the backbone. They reach everywhere in the body. They "step on the gas" wherever they reach, and adjust the parts they reach to work harder— for example, dilating the arteries in a hard-working arm.

But as with Mary's little lamb who went everywhere Mary did, a parasympathetic fiber goes everywhere a sympathetic fiber goes. (*Para* means "lying beside.") The parasympathetic fibers fan out from roughly the top quarter and bottom quarter of the backbone, and tag along to step on the brakes at every place the other section steps on the gas. Which section is boss at the moment determines pretty much how the organ, or involuntary muscle, will be operating—whether it will be energetically speeding up, lethargically slowing down, or in a nicely balanced steady state.

What Dr. Lowenstein did was to tackle those sections of the autonomics that reach the pupil of the eye. A simple, yet brilliant idea: flash a light briefly on the pupil to contract it, keep flashing the light every four seconds, and see how the balance between the sympathetic and parasympathetic sections holds up under a steady workout. This is similar to stop-and-go driving, fifteen times a minute, to test

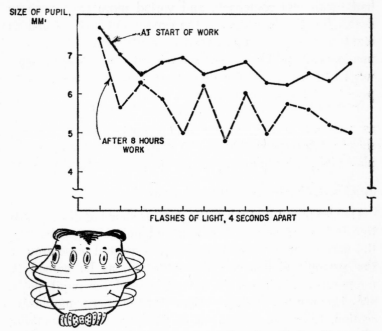

SIZE OF PUPIL, MM'

AT START OF WORK

AFTER 8 HOURS WORK

FLASHES OF LIGHT, 4 SECONDS APART

Data from Dr. Otto Lowenstein

The pupils of the eyes had less comeback after flashes of light following a day's work

an automobile's ability to stand up under punishment of that sort.

He found that the pupil grew sluggish, lost its recuperative power, or became tired out, on successive flashes as the steady work disrupted the balance in the autonomics. The way the pupil slacked off told much about the person's tired feelings in general. For instance, the pupil revealed that tired feelings gather headway in the invisible changes some time before the person begins to feel that he is tired.

The chartoon shows what effect a day of white-collar work had on the pupil's comeback to the flashes. The pupil had much less comeback, and varied more from flash to flash, after the 16 people in the experiment had finished an eight-hour day of their regular white-jacket work in a medical college. The clashes and restrictiveness of their day's work had weakened the delicate balance between the opposed sections of the autonomics.

From his years of research on some 3000 people—as well as with cats and monkeys—Dr. Lowenstein concludes that shifts or disorganization of the activity of the autonomics play a large part in giving normal people their tired feelings.

3. Restitution—restoring the balance

He also found that when the pupil is showing disorganization in the autonomics, it can be suddenly changed back to the normal steady condition if an unexpected noise arouses the person's vigilance. This *restitution*, as he named it, temporarily eliminates the sluggishness of the pupil, probably because the vigilance stimulates the energy-mobilizing section. Likewise, excitement or thinking about something pleasant or interesting, was found to eliminate the telltale signs of tiredness in the pupil's reactions to the stressing series of light flashes.

Office managers apply the principle of restitution when they give clerks some tasks which interest them to "snap them out of their tiredness." Work that is challenging can "restitute."

So can play. The attorney worn to a frazzle by a sedentary but trying day in court becomes a restituted person on the golf links where he can wham the ball (express hostility) the way he wanted to sock the opposing attorney (clashes and restrictiveness) earlier that afternoon.

4. The rowing crew and their coach

A series of tests on oarsmen in a collegiate boat crew showed how disorganization of the ductless glands, which in some ways are similar to the autonomics in their functions, can be added to the disruption due to hard visible activity. Thus anxiety, clashes, and restrictiveness often make people more tired than their visible activity warrants, as is shown at the right end of the diagram "How Tired Feelings Originate."

Dr. S. Richardson Hill and ten colleagues—physiologists, biochemists, psychiatrists, psychologists—checked on the boat crew while the men were practicing for the race, and again right after they had competed in the race. Rowing in a race is one of the most exhausting forms of muscle exertion, so exhausting that the average oarsman worked off from six to eight pounds during this 4-mile race. It is grueling physical work that can produce feelings of profound tiredness without any emotional stress being added.

The crucial part of the rowing story for us was that the emotional stress of being in an actual race produced more marked glandular changes than when the same men rowed equally strenuously in practice runs. Being up against competition, and playing for keeps rather than for fun, added some anxiety stresses to the exertion of rowing. And when the crew lost the race, some stress from frustration and disappointment was added.

But note this: The team's coach and the coxswain, who did none of the rowing but merely "went along for the ride," had about the same glandular disruption as the hard-working oarsmen did. The coach and coxswain had plenty of invisible activity, and may have felt keener anxiety about the outcome of the race than the crew did—their glands had a right to be out of balance.

There are periods in one's life when the glands are likely to become unbalanced for a time. During the teen years, for example, the maturing of the sex glands is usually accompanied by a general but temporary disruption of the balance. Again in middle life, there is usually another disruption during the climacteric, or change of life, which may affect men as well as women.

There is usually an increase in tired feelings at both of these periods in life.

The stories about the pupil of the eye, and the crew and coach, should give the white-collar person a new perspective on his tired feelings. He has a right to be tired. His invisible activities can disorganize the use of his energies as seriously as hard manual labor can. Although he still has the strength and energy, they are not much use to him as long as he is switched to conserve energy and feels tired out.

This applies to chronic tiredness, also. Dr. Benjamin Kissin has summed up the findings of his research group as follows: "Our tests indicate that in chronic white-collar tiredness there is an imbalance in autonomic nervous system activity. There was overactivity of the parasympathetic sections, and underactivity of the sympathetic section. . . . Our data also indicate a functional underactivity of the entire system of ductless glands."

5. Implications for mastering tired feelings

Employers usually plan work so it will consume as little energy as possible. Jobs are simplified, steps and motions reduced, machinery is used to do the heavy parts of a job. These changes do cut down on the human energy expenditure, and usually increase output by saving time.

But these changes do not always reduce tired feelings. Sometimes tired feelings are actually increased because the changes cause boredom (monotony) or resentment (hostility) in the workers. We will find shortly that there are many things employers can do to reduce tired feelings, but this is accomplished mostly by cutting down personal irritations (clashes and restrictiveness) rather than by saving calories of energy.

Employers should think more about cutting down the irritations of the glands and autonomics in addition to reducing the foot-pounds of lifting done. And the worker will help himself to feel less tired if he stews less about irritations, annoyances, restrictions, and other personal difficulties which keep his glands and autonomics on edge so that the use of his personal powers is blocked.

We will delve deeper into this as the book goes on. A word is in order at this time, however, for those who do sedentary work. That includes all white-collar workers and a large share of blue-collar. And the word should be a strong one. Sedentary working and living causes many internal changes which interfere with the use of one's energy. The steady state becomes sluggish, so to speak, and the person operates at a low level of physiological efficiency. As a result, the sedentary person seldom masters his tired feelings by resting more. Paradoxically, he will feel more energetic if he uses more energy.

Instead of trying to save his energies, the sedentary person would be better off—feel less tired—if he lifted, pushed, pulled, and grunted more to limber up his steady state. This is so important in our modern world that we will devote a separate book to it. For the time being, keep in mind these words of Dr. Theodore G. Klumpp at the Seattle meeting of the American Medical Association:

"Over and over again it has been demonstrated that physical activity at the end of a trying but sedentary day brings a degree of refreshment and renewed energy that nothing else can equal."

There are some important differences between sedentary, or white-collar, tired feelings, and those following muscular work. The following chapter explains the differences between them.

CHAPTER 8

The tiredness twins

1. How tired feelings hit white-collar people

In everyday life the tired feelings from visible activity and invisible activity are mixed together, the mixture changing from situation to situation. With the rowing crew, the feelings came mostly from physical work on practice days, but on race day a sizable amount of nerve and gland disorganization was added.

In industry, some day laborers' tiredness is mostly the result of their visible activity, but other laborers on the same job have clashes and restrictions in addition which complicate their tired feelings and make restitution more difficult.

Whether the tired feelings become a problem depends

not upon how much they have to use their muscles, but what attitudes their inner selves happen to have toward the situations at the time. The boss's handling of the men, and how well they get along together, usually have much to do

From the booklet "The Worry-Go-Round." Courtesy The Connecticut Mutual Life Insurance Co.

A great deal of invisible activity in glands and nerves can be produced by lack of self-confidence in certain situations, so that the balance shifts to put on the brakes and the person "feels all out of energy"

with these attitudes—but so does the individual's own outlook and expectations.

By and large, the manual laborer is not plagued by clashes and frustrations as severely as is the more ambitious white-collar man who hopes to win friends and climb up the ladder—if his tired feelings do not interfere with reaching these cherished aims. Sales people, office workers, executives, teachers, professional people, proprietors, and a large share of assembly-line workers, grow tired mostly because of clashes and restrictions. But there may also be a slight amount of tiredness from visible activity mixed in from time to time. On the day the office clerk had to run for the bus, for example, the visible activity upset her steady state. She had trouble getting her breath and her hands were shaky for an hour after she reached the office.

The sales person who has to be on his feet most of the day will usually accumulate some loss of strength in leg and back muscles as the day goes on—"My feet are killing me!"— as well as other tired feelings from visible activity.

Despite the fact that the tiredness twins are usually mixed together, there are some differences between them we should know about to keep from getting mixed up about our tiredness.

2. How to tell the tiredness twins apart

Our tired feelings, whether from muscular exertion or from clashes and restrictions, are much alike in their end results: we feel too tuckered out to keep on with what we have been doing, or to start something new.

When that stage is reached we may do nothing. Or, we may change to some other work and forget that we were worn out a few minutes previously—different work may restitute a person by using different muscles in the case of energy depletion, or by distracting him from his clashes and restrictions in the other case.

These two varieties of the same over-all feeling of tiredness might be compared to twins who are so much alike that strangers can't tell them apart. But the relatives who have observed the twins a long time can detect real differences between them. These twin tirednesses, too, have slight differences which can be spotted when one knows what to look for. Here is a tabulation of some of the more usual ways in which each of the twin tirednesses seems to reveal its own peculiar characteristics.

Tired feelings from muscular labor ("Blue-collar" twin)	*Tired feelings from clashes and restrictions* ("White-collar" twin)
1. Often "feels good," seldom painful for experienced workers	1. Usually unpleasant, because hostility, despair, are mixed in
2. Increases as work is continued	2. Comes and goes, sometimes suddenly; worn out one minute, rested the next
3. Felt mostly in muscles that have been used	3. Likely to be felt all over; difficult to think
4. Does not prevent motivation to go on with the work as soon as rested up	4. Weakens motivation; inclines to turn to other work, or to do nothing
5. Disappear after rest pause, or night's sleep	5. Often not relieved by rest, sleep, or vacation; may become chronic
6. Taken for granted and not fretted about	6. Produce distress, often leading to resort to tonics, food fads, etc.

3. Why tired feelings from invisible activities are worse

The last three items in these lists have an important practical message for white-collar people. They reveal why the white-collar variety of tiredness is likely to be self-perpetuating, unless the vicious circle is broken.

This tiredness often persists despite rest, vitamins, sun baths, massage, and what not that people try, because the memory of the clashes and restrictions lingers on and keeps up the disorganizing effects on both glands and nerves.

The office worker may continue to wear himself down during rest pauses, or after work, by stewing thoughts about office politics. His sleep may be poor because he takes gnawing worries about job pressures to bed with him. When he

From the booklet "Needlepoint." Courtesy The Connecticut Mutual Life Insurance Co.

Tired feelings springing from clashes and restrictions often persist simply because the invisible activity lingers on after one presumably stops work, as with this woman who feels restricted because she is not able to buy what she would like to. We would suspect that she is tired out more by envy than by the broom

gets up in the morning he does not really start a new day. The same old clashes and restrictions are revived and at the thought of them tiredness envelops him as he reluctantly drags himself off to check in for his daily rat race, as he calls it.

In contrast, the day laborer is more likely to awaken fresh as a daisy, if his ambitions are satisfied by having a steady job. If he gets along with his boss and fellow workers, there are good chances that he will actually be eager to get to the job where he can get the good feeling of doing something with his muscles.

In his effort to get ahead in the white-collar world, however, the ambitious person will inevitably often be disorganized by clashes and restrictions. They can't all be dodged. He should expect to have a share of white-collar tiredness on occasions. If he has sufficient self-direction he can learn to continue his work regardless of the tired feelings—restitute himself by work to master the feelings.

Fighting back at restrictions by overworry about them can be more insidious than overwork. When the white-collar person decides to tolerate the inevitable clashes and restrictions, he will usually discover that he no longer tires out as easily.

How tired should you get on a white-collar job? Just as tired as you allow clashes and restrictions to make you.

Feeling tired, as the next chapter shows, is a signal to do something. Exactly what should be done depends upon which tiredness twin predominates in the feeling.

CHAPTER 9

The essential function of tired feelings

1. THEY WARN US TO PROTECT OURSELVES
2. WHEN "PEP PILLS" ARE USED
3. THE NATURAL RESPONSE TO THE WARNING IS BEHIND THE TIMES
4. HOW RUTH B. ADJUSTED TO A TIRING SITUATION
5. WHEN TIRED FEELINGS HAVE A SECONDARY FUNCTION

1. They warn us to protect ourselves

We should be thankful that we can feel tired, for tired feelings have an essential function.

Many biologists believe we have tired feelings because they proved beneficial during the long course of evolution. Creatures that did not have tired feelings when they had some ailment, for instance, might not slow down enough to give their bodies a fair chance to conquer the ailment. Thus they would die off earlier than creatures that did feel tired on such occasions. During the course of centuries there would be more descendants of creatures born with systems that did develop tired feelings when ailments occurred.

It was probably much the same with tired feelings that came with hard physical work. Creatures that did not have built-in warnings to tell them when to stop might keep on working until they dropped from physical exhaustion. On the other hand, those who had tired feelings would be prompted to ease up in time to survive. The feelings may have been uncomfortable, but they gave these creatures a survival advantage and they were less likely to disappear from the earth.

Something of that sort probably accounts for mankind's, and all higher animals', proclivity to feel tired when rest is needed. Whatever the origin during the course of time, it is now true that *tired feelings are almost always a warning sign that something is wrong and should be corrected.*

Tired feelings are not always a perfect warning, however. There are some diseases, such as some forms of tuberculosis, which do not give rise to the feelings until the disorder is well advanced. But hard physical work almost always touches off the warning in ample time to protect the well-being of the organism—unless a person has taken pep pills, or happens to have supermotivation which leads him to ignore the warning and keep on working, as happens in maniacal states.

2. When "pep pills" are used

The value of a timely warning to let down is dramatically demonstrated in some of the effects that are produced when people use pep pills.

These pills do not provide any energy or nourishment. Nor do the pills make much difference in the feelings of tiredness when taken in ordinary doses when not working, as was the case with the men in the first chartoon. These men spent the day in an air-conditioned lounge, reading, writing, and talking. They did not have chronic tired feelings to begin with, and the pills had no significant effect on their tired feelings.

What the pills seem to do when a person is working is to stimulate him for a few hours. Usually the person works and moves faster after taking an ordinary dose, as the upper output curve in the second chartoon shows.

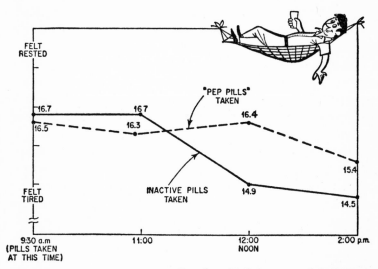

Data from R. G. Pearson and G. E. Byars

The "pep pills" had only a slight effect on their tired feelings when the men spent the time relaxing

The pills do not dissolve the underlying cause of the tired feelings—usually the contrary, in fact. When stimulated by the pep pill, the person overworks and thus generally makes the situation worse. Instead of resting in the case of physical work, or straightening out his personal problems if clashes and restrictions are the root of the trouble, he plunges ahead in a nonadaptive fashion. The feelings are not mastered.

This is illustrated by Dr. Peter H. Knapp's account of

Olga V., a nurse. She had been in a lifelong clash with her mother, whom she hated. Olga married impulsively, but soon separated—another clash. Then she became mixed up in triangular love affairs—restrictive situations she could not resolve at the time. In view of all this inner stress, she

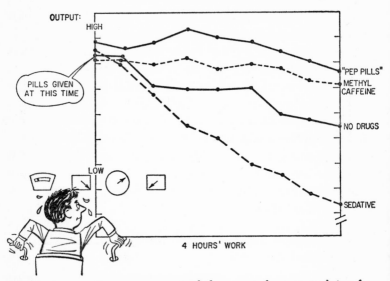

Work was a continuous movement of three controls so as to bring four steadily shifting pointers back to zero.

Data from Drs. G. T. Hauty and R. B. Payne.

How "pep pills" and other drugs affected output at trying work

naturally developed oversized tired feelings, along with anxiety and depressed moods. But she had to work, so she began to use pep pills to keep herself going. "I needed them for my work," she said. By age 30 she was taking them steadily, and in large amounts, as many as eight at a time. Those giant doses kept her going without a stop. She held down two jobs at once, and sometimes worked 72 hours at a stretch. Nice not to have tired feelings and be able to work like that?

Let's look at the other side of the ledger before answering. She worked off 60 pounds. Her heart rate became very rapid. She had spells of breathlessness. Her skin became itchy and she scratched until her arms were covered with sores. Her muscles became trembly. All in all, her steady state was in a bad state.

"You know what a plane is like at the end of the runway just before it takes off," she said; "it races the motor and for a minute it seems as if it will shake itself apart. That's the way I feel after I load up on the pills."

The function of tired feelings is to warn us so we do not shake ourselves apart. Pep pills merely "whip a tired horse," and do nothing to ease the clashes and restrictions. Clearly the pills are no help for adapting to, or changing, the principal causes of tired feelings. They may help the work, but they harm the person.

3. The natural response to the warning is behind the times

There has been a lot of shadow boxing in the fight against tired feelings. People have tackled the wrong enemies, as was illustrated by the office managers. Or, they have used the wrong weapons on the real enemies. The sedentary person who takes more rest when he should probably get more exercise is an example of this.

Here is the story of why the apparently inborn response to tired feelings is behind the times and attacks the wrong enemies. We recall that the feelings were useful in the long struggle for survival, warning against the threats of disease or overdoing. The proper response to those threats was to slow down instead of racing the engine.

Slowing down, or resting, is still the natural response to tired feelings, whatever their cause. But because the conditions of life have long since changed, the feelings are seldom due to threats to our bodily well-being from overwork or disease. Instead, as man has developed into a social being with thoughts, hopes, ideals, the tired feelings have come to be touched off also by threats to the human spirit. Resting, or inaction, is seldom adaptive when a clash or restrictive situation touches off the warning, but we tend to respond that way, just as our remote ancestors did when such a response was useful.

Tired feelings are a normal part of the ups-and-downs of life, particularly of the downs which seem to threaten an individual's self-realization. Moreover, tired feelings are here to stay. We have this built-in warning system, and life has ample clashes and restrictions to bring it forth.

All would be fine if people would make the right response to the warnings of threats to the human spirit, instead of the old but natural response which is behind the times. The tired feeling from a personality clash is not a false feeling, but the natural response is likely to be false. Eunice H.'s story, in Chapter 4, provided an example. Walking helped her master her attacks of tired feelings, but the natural response made her feel too tired to walk. So she just rested more, and merely put on weight rather than mastering the tired feelings.

With modern life and work what they are, we have to figure what the warning is about if we are to make the tired feelings our good friends. We have to teach ourselves some new responses that are more suitable for modern life than the primitive one of desisting from activity.

4. How Ruth B. adjusted to a tiring situation

Mrs. Ruth B., whose tired feelings were studied by Dr. Edward A. Burkhardt, illustrates how it is usually essential to do something besides rest to cope with the feelings.

In middle life she began to have severe tired feelings, and a few pains she presumed were due to gallstones. She blamed her tiredness on the gallstones. Medical tests disclosed no gallstones, however, or any other ailment that would make her tired.

Why so tired, then? The physician encouraged her to talk about any secret problems she might have, and an unusual story came out. She was caught in a restrictive situation she could not solve and which threatened her inner self. Six months after she had married a wealthy man he died unexpectedly, leaving no will. There was a long lawsuit which brought her a settlement of a $250 monthly income —and a bill from her lawyer for $3000. A somewhat strainful situation, but no special tired feelings bothered her yet.

Soon she married a bank vice president, but did not tell him about her monthly income, or that she owed her lawyer and could not pay him. Apparently it was true love for the banker, because he had not looked into her financial status. After being the banker's wife for a couple of months her tired feelings began to snowball until they made her desperate. When she tried to rest she could not relax because of thoughts about the lawyer's bill, and what her banker husband might think when, as was inevitable, he learned about it. A month of this was all she could stand, so she went to a physician about "gallstones," which she was sure were the reason for her tiredness.

After discussing her predicament with the physician she decided to make peace with her inner self. She would use her personal jewelry, which was appraised at $2000, to pay the lawyer, if he would settle for that. He would. Then, to clear up everything, she told her banker husband about the monthly income and the lawyer's bill she had paid.

Those actions dissolved the restricting situation. Life began again for Ruth B., this time without those tired feelings. The natural response of resting did not help solve the threatening situation.

5. When tired feelings have a secondary function

A touch of tired feelings seems to be ever present if we look for it, but generally the feeling is not noticed until the warning is strong enough to cry for some action. A few persons, however, have a quirk which leads them to make the most of the faint tired feelings most of us ignore most of the time.

There was Horace P., a brilliant engineer and bachelor who landed excellent jobs but soon quit them because he got too tired to continue the work. Between jobs, which was most of the time, he lounged around the house, depending upon his doting mother to take care of him.

When Dr. Henry P. Laughlin studied this engineer's tiredness, it was obvious that the man had what is known as a dependent character. Since early childhood he had felt that the world owed him a living. Most "constitutionally lazy" people who feel threatened if they have to take care of themselves have that quirk in their inner selves.

Laziness and sponging off others, however, is not generally approved; tiredness is approved, because of the misbelief that it is due to hard work. So if the dependent person makes the most of his faint tired feelings, he can justify his proclivity to take life easy. What this engineer was unconsciously thinking in his private world, Dr. Laughlin reports, was: "Because I am chronically tired, surely I cannot be expected to support myself and measure up to adult standards. Mother must take care of me."

It is usually difficult to alter this type of quirk that Horace P. had, but with the help of a behavior specialist he was able to adjust the deep-seated dependent attitude of his inner self so that he no longer took advantage of his tired feelings to take advantage of others. He married, set up his own home, no longer complained of chronic tiredness, and became more steady in his professional work.

There are also some persons who happen to learn that by magnifying their tired feelings they can get sympathy, or avoid doing disliked tasks, or possibly be regarded as conscientious employees who have overworked. They may not have lazy quirks, but they have simply learned that some reward will be theirs if they feel "too tired to do it."

Some learn to take such advantage of tired feelings while they are convalescing from an illness. As Dr. John Romano has pointed out, they may find lolling around and being cared for so enjoyable that they are loath to resume a more active and self-reliant life—they learn to have chronic tiredness because it was rewarding during their convalescence. This is one reason physicians nowadays like to have patients get up and around without coddling as soon as possible; also to avoid the handicaps that come from being too sedentary.

Are the tired feelings imaginary in these instances where people use the magnified feeling to get them some advantage they enjoy? Usually these people have sufficient personal reasons for feeling tired, even when they have not done a lick of work. They can sincerely feel tired, with no pretense about it. But they almost never know what it is that makes them want to take advantage of the feelings.

Once they get some insight into their deep motives (such as a dependent character), or how they learned to feel that way (as by being a spoiled brat), adjustment generally becomes a fairly simple matter. The rehabilitation of Horace P. is an example. It often requires skilled help from a specialist to lead the individual to understand why he likes to take advantage of being tired. In some instances, however, the specialist cannot make headway because the person has come to enjoy the advantages being tired give him so much that he resists changing.

All this raises the question: "How can we be sure any person feels tired?" That is the topic for the next chapter.

CHAPTER 10

How can we tell when a person feels tired?

---

1. ONLY YOU KNOW IF YOU FEEL TIRED
2. DECLINING MUSCLE STRENGTH AS TIME GOES ON
3. HEART-RATE RECOVERY AFTER VISIBLE ACTIVITY
4. SLUMPS IN WORK OUTPUT

1. Only you know if you feel tired

Two things are likely to mislead us when we try to tell how tired another person feels. (1) There are other feelings which are often mistaken for tired feelings; reluctance to do something, for example. (2) Tired feelings are a personal experience—an "inside feeling"—which cannot be seen by onlookers, and which are also extremely difficult for the person himself to describe.

So it behooves us to take apart these complicated feelings, and mixtures of feelings, to get a better working knowledge of them. In this and the following three chapters we will take up the natural history of tired feelings, to get inside information about an inside feeling.

It has been found almost impossible to size up tired feelings from the outside by watching a person. There are some occasions, of course, when a person "looks tired" or "acts tired" and also feels that way. But even these may be misleading. Abraham Lincoln, for instance, frequently looked tired. His movements slowed down, he became careless, his face drooped, nothing seemed to interest him, and he would sit and rest for days in a row. During these periods he not only felt profoundly tired, but also gloomy and depressed. We can't be positive whether the "looks" at such times are due to the depressed mood, or to the tired feelings, or to both.

Feeling tired and feeling gloomy are close relatives and often occur together as well as looking alike on the outside. This may be because both varieties can be touched off by some situations which the person sees as threatening or restricting him, as Chapter 12 will explain.

About the only times we can be certain by looking at him that a person feels tired is when he is so worn out that he drops in his tracks. There are rare instances of physical exhaustion when a person's steady state is so far off balance that he collapses. Then he becomes weak—"strength completely gone"—he sweats profusely, his heart races, his breathing is difficult, he may become sick to his stomach, and he is dizzy unless he lies down. He usually does lie down right where he is, if he doesn't fall down first. This unmistakable picture of extreme tiredness is seen only after the hardest work the individual can do, such as shoveling wet snow, manual labor in a hot foundry, or running in a cross-country race.

In everyday life and work it is almost never possible to tell if people are tired by looking at them. Some can feel dog tired and not show it. Some look tired, but aren't. Others deliberately conceal their tired feelings by acting the opposite. Actors, and especially ballet dancers, may feel dog tired but act the peppy role the public expects of them—"the show must go on." Some executives, too, keep their tiredness a secret by acting as they believe dynamic business people should act—"it's good business not to appear tired."

Because we seldom look as tired as we feel, even when we are not trying to hide it, we are not likely to be given the consideration or sympathetic help we want and need when we do feel tired.

Only the person himself knows how tired he feels.

2. Declining muscle strength as time goes on

Isn't there some inside information we can get without having to take the person's word for how tired he feels?

The earliest experiments aimed to get such information by measuring the decline in strength of muscles used in some particular work. When the strength declined it was assumed the person felt tired. But, people being as they are, they often feel genuinely tired when their strength has not declined in the least. Also, the decline in muscle strength may not be due solely to the condition of the muscle. The individual's motivation to exert his full strength can make a big difference, as was illustrated by the chartoon of the men hanging on, in Chapter 1. And Dr. E. S. Roush has found that when people are hypnotized they do not have as much decline in strength.

Tests of decline in muscle strength can be given easily, as the variety sketched in the first chartoon illustrates. Such tests have revealed a great deal about conditions which help a person acquire the sustained strength needed for muscular work, and also about methods of working which make the least demand on muscles. An example of the second is Dr.

H. Harrison Clarke's tests of footwear for the U.S. Army. There was least decline in strength of leg and foot muscles when ankle-height shoes were worn, most decline when low-cut shoes were worn.

Data from Dr. Muriel H. Stern

Less "sustained strength" by those who were ill but could be up and around

Testing the loss of muscle strength is applicable only to those jobs where hard muscular work is done. Few jobs— fewer each year—use any muscles enough to produce a decline in their strength during a work spell. People can feel very tired without having moved a muscle.

3. Heart-rate recovery after visible activity

Heart rate is another tangible measurement that has been used to get inside information about tiredness. We remember that the heart speeds up as physical work goes on, bringing fresh oxygen and blood sugar to restore the steady state in the working muscle. The higher the heart rate goes as a result of physical exertion, the more demanding the work has been.

In addition, when the exertion is stopped, the heart rate drops rapidly back toward normal. How rapidly it drops during the first three minutes after stopping work was found in the Harvard Fatigue Laboratory to give a good indication of

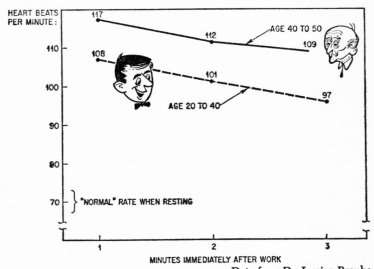

Data from Dr. Lucien Brouha

The heart rates of the older men did not recover as rapidly after the moderate work

how demanding (tiring?) the work had been. It drops back to normal more rapidly when the work is less demanding.

Both of those effects are illustrated in the second chartoon which is based on men doing moderately heavy work on their regular jobs. It is significant that, although both groups had done the same physical work, it placed less demand on the hearts of the younger men. The older men's hearts had to beat more rapidly while doing the work, and in addition they did not slow down as much when the work was stopped. This suggests strongly that (1) the work was more tiring to the older men, and (2) that the older men needed a longer rest period, perhaps more frequent rest periods.

The heart-rate speed-up while working, and the recovery rate while resting, are present only when physical work is done. White-collar workers have these effects only when they run for the bus, climb stairs, bowl, or engage in other off-the-job activities which are good for them. They can feel genuinely tired on the job without their hearts changing a bit.

As Dr. Lucien Brouha told a conference of the Society for the Advancement of Management: "The unmeasurable factors which cause stress and fatigue in industry, such as emotional stimuli, boredom, social adjustments, are certainly more numerous than those which can be measured."

4. Slumps in work output

Work output is a tangible measurement which has been tried in hopes of getting inside information about tired feelings. Hour-by-hour output records have been accumulated by the thousands, and it was taken for granted that if output slumped one hour, it was because the workers felt tired.

Slumps in output, however, have turned out to be one of the most misleading indicators of tired feelings. This is clearly brought out by the third chartoon, which shows the records of people who were doing monotonous light work that used no more energy an hour than a half a salted peanut would supply. The top line shows that output remained high during the five-hour shift. Yet the workers were actually feeling more tired every twenty minutes, as the bottom line pictures. The boss would not have guessed this by looking at their output. Only the workers knew how tired they felt.

Output remained high, despite increasing tiredness, because the people were especially motivated in this experiment to push themselves and keep turning out all they could. On most regular jobs, in contrast, workers are not motivated to push themselves that much.

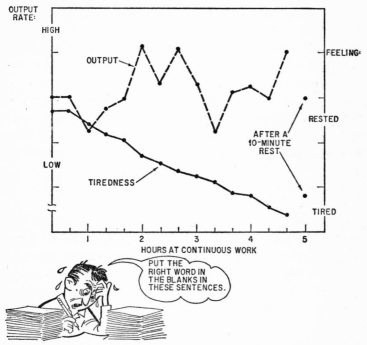

Data from Dr. A. T. Poffenberger

The boss couldn't tell how tired they were (Their feelings of tiredness got worse, but their output did not)

This particular experiment had considerable influence in shifting the study of tired feelings from output curves to the feelings themselves. Output curves may occasionally be in step with the feelings, but in general they give misleading answers about the true state of affairs. There are several reasons for this deceptiveness.

Workers can feel dog tired yet keep up their output without any risk to their energies, on most jobs.

The opposite is also true. Workers can feel "fresh as daisies," yet have intermittent slumps in output.

The worst cause of the misleading, however, is that on about half of factory jobs (a smaller share of office jobs) the workers, as Dr. S. B. Mathewson found, hold their daily output down to what they consider "a fair day's work." The low output at any hour does not necessarily mean they feel tired; it usually means they have accumulated a "bank" or "kitty," as they call it behind the boss's back, so they voluntarily slow down to keep from turning out more work that day than the work group thought was fair enough for the company. This deliberate holding down of daily output takes place even when workers are paid at piece rates. Such output curves tell little about tired feelings, but a great deal about workers' attitudes toward work and the company.

All in all, the only way we can find out how tired a person feels is to ask him. Will he be able to tell us accurately?

CHAPTER 11

Feelings often confused with tired feelings

1. TIRED FEELINGS HAVE MANY SIDES
2. MUSCLE SENSATIONS MAY PLAY A PART
3. DROWSINESS WITHOUT FEELING TIRED
4. LAZINESS IS ENJOYED, TIRED FEELINGS ARE NOT

1. Tired feelings have many sides

When we ask the man who has them, he may not be able to tell us much about his tired feelings. "Just feel tired out, and have to rest," may be all he can report. Tired feelings are such vague and diffuse experiences it is difficult to describe them.

It would be easier if there were some definite sensation of tiredness, like the sensations from a sore finger. But there is no specific sensation of tiredness. Tired feelings are a pool, or mixture, of feelings that often come together; depression and tired feelings, for instance, are closely related and tend to be intermixed.

Knowing when you are tired, and how tired, is also complicated by the fact that tired feelings have several varieties,

87

as well as sizes. The variety or characteristics of the feelings are worth knowing about because they can give clues to the underlying cause. Sizes and locations, to be taken up in Chapter 13, can also give strong hints about how to master them.

We should speak of *those* tired feelings, instead of using the words tiredness or fatigue, which are names for abstractions. Fatigue is no longer considered a unitary thing or independent element. Most scientists look upon the word "fatigue" as conveying misleading conceptions and avoid using the word, as we try to avoid using it in this book; but, language being what it is, the naughty word slips in a few times.

To get at the root of tired feelings we should understand how they are further complicated by three somewhat similar experiences which often intrude, or are mixed in with them. These are: sensations from muscles, drowsiness, and laziness.

2. Muscle sensations may play a part

Everyone is receiving messages from muscles and joints all the time. These messages give rise to dim sensations that are often mixed in with tired feelings. This is especially so when one is doing hard manual work; the experienced worker uses these as a signal to stop and rest before his muscles become sore or stiff. The sensations may also be a factor in tired feelings with people doing light work, but who work in a constrained posture. Typing is an example of this. The working fingers seldom feel tired. Typists complain about tired feelings in neck and shoulder, as the chartoon pictures. Those nonworking muscles become sore, not tired, because necks and shoulders are held too stiffly. The continued tenseness produces muscle sensations that become intense enough for the typist to notice.

If people would move around more while they are doing repetitive work, they would be less likely to notice muscle and joint sensations which they call feeling tired.

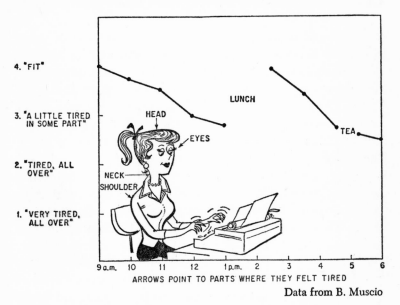

ARROWS POINT TO PARTS WHERE THEY FELT TIRED

Data from B. Muscio

How tired the typists felt during the day's work

Most muscle sensations are not clearly noticed. Many people, in fact, are never aware they have such sensations until they sprain an ankle, or notice that an arm "feels strangely different" after sawing a few boards. It is probably such sensations that make feeling weary different from simply feeling tired. In weariness the muscle sensations are more marked; we feel weariness in the body. The muscle sensations are also looked upon as some of the seasoning that is sprinkled into the tired feelings. Sometimes they give a pleasant seasoning, as in golf, other times unpleasant, as with the typists.

For a while it was assumed that the muscle and joint sensations were, in effect, the tired feelings. It is true that we are in a mood to notice these sensations when we feel tired. But we can be genuinely tired without any increase in mus-

From booklet "The Worry-Go-Round." Courtesy The Connecticut Mutual Life Insurance Co.

This man will be a good candidate for tired feelings, and we would not expect them to be complicated by muscle sensations. If he gets tired feelings, they will come from invisible activity of autonomics and glands, not from muscular activity

cle sensations. We can notice the sensations in an arm muscle we have overworked, yet not feel tired: so we may turn eagerly to other work that does not involve the sensitive arm. When an individual feels tired, in contrast, he doesn't feel like working.

The largest share of tired feelings are due to personality clashes and restrictiveness. Those situation should not increase muscle and joint sensations. When we are "aching tired" something has been added to the clash or restrictiveness.

3. Drowsiness without feeling tired

Drowsiness is a close imitator of feeling tired.

Moderate spells of drowsiness come over the average adult about every 70 minutes during his working hours. With some people it is every 50 minutes, with others 90 minutes, etc. Each drowsy spell lasts only a few minutes, as a rule. The drowsiness tends to be stronger every two or three hours. That is when some workers may fall asleep at their desks, or yearn for a "sleep break," or walk around vigorously to "shake off the drowsiness." Probably one worker out of ten is so built that he needs a sleep break during working hours. After a person reaches age 50, it becomes more difficult for him to fight off these daytime drowsy spells.

These spells are due to our built-in rhythm of sleep-and-wakefulness which shifts the balance of the autonomics from the energy-mobilizing to the energy-saving sections. This shift is quite similar to that described in Dr. Lowenstein's experiments on the pupil of the eye, in Chapter 7, but it is different in three important respects.

(1) The shift to drowsiness is timed primarily by a pre-set rhythm which operates automatically and appears to be inborn; it will shift to drowsiness without any help from visible or invisible activity. (2) The network of nerves involved does not vary much from person to person; there are not as marked individual differences in "that drowsy feeling" as there are in those tired feelings. (3) The electrical waves from the brain are slowed down during these drowsy

periods; tired feelings have not been found to produce any characteristic change in brain waves.

Drowsy spells have their own distinctive features which are not like those tired feelings, and which can be summarized:

> Arms and legs feel "heavy," or limp, and it is difficult to move them, although there is an impulse to yawn and stretch.
>
> When drowsy we become "groggy" and senses are dulled; we may misunderstand what people say, or not hear them; reading matter may look blurred.
>
> The mind wanders in the direction of daydreams, and we may "see things"; one private secretary "saw" her boss standing in the doorway, although he was out of town.
>
> Drowsy people are overtaken by a "don't care" spirit and become less vigilant to avoid errors and dangers.
>
> The body is likely to feel itchy and slightly warm at first, but chilly a few minutes later as the flow of blood is changed at the body surface.

Dr. Edgar M. Haverland studied one man throughout six weeks in a factor-analysis experiment on varieties of fatigue. The man was tested a total of 75 times on 49 different aspects of tired feelings. It was found that the drowsiness factor affected his performance so that he became inaccurate, did not memorize as well, and was slower to make decisions in some of the tests.

In the meaning used in this book, we do not consider these drowsy spells as tired feelings, because drowsy people often fight off sleep and try to keep on with their work or play.

To avoid errors and accidents, however, drowsy periods are a proper time for coffee breaks, especially when that stronger wave of sleepiness strikes every two or three hours. But perhaps your coffee break companions do not have their drowsy spells at the same time you do.

There is more information on drowsiness in our book *Sound Ways to Sound Sleep.*

4. Laziness is enjoyed, tired feelings are not

Laziness also has much superficial resemblance to feeling tired. Some lazy people take advantage of this to avoid being called "goldbrickers" or "work shirkers," claiming they are really "all tired out." This is a secondary function we met in Chapter 9.

On the other hand, people who honestly are tired out are sometimes mistakenly called lazy by acquaintances who cannot understand why they should feel tired. Many share-croppers in the southern states were scornfully called lazy and shiftless, for example, until it was discovered that hook-worms produced bodily conditions which gave ample reasons for "not having the energy to work."

There is one outstanding difference between the lazy person and the tired person. The lazy one has what psycho-analysts call a dependent character, which appears to have been fixed in some people when they were weaned in infancy. The person who has this dependent make-up believes the world owes him a living without having to work for it, and he lives up to this belief as well as he can—"not the working type." In contrast, the tired person thinks he should work, even though he may not feel like it when he is tired.

Lincoln called himself lazy, but he wasn't lazy in this sense because he felt he should work for his living. But Horace P., the engineer described in Chapter 9, was an example of the dependent, or lazy, character.

There are also some minor differences. The lazy person tends to be carefree and enjoys being idle; to him life is for loafing or playing. The tired person, on the other hand, seldom enjoys having to rest, has little enthusiasm for play, and prefers to be busy at making a living.

The tired person is also inclined to worry about "something wrong" with him that makes him tired. And he wants to get rid of his tired feelings. But the lazy person worries only that people may criticize him for being lazy, and he does not worry much about that; he seldom wants to change his indolent streak and wishes he had been born rich.

Muscle sensations, drowsiness, and, in some people, laziness, are parts of the mixture a person calls "feeling tired." There is one essential ingredient in the mixture, and we take that up next.

CHAPTER **12**

The distinctive mark of tired feelings

1. DESPAIR—THE BIG BROTHER OF TIRED FEELINGS
2. OTHER REACTIONS TO FRUSTRATING SITUATIONS
3. THE YEARNING FOR SYMPATHETIC HELP
4. TIRED FEELINGS COOL OFF THE WILL TO WORK
5. "TOO TIRED TO EAT ... OR TO TALK"

1. Despair—the big brother of tired feelings

Muscle sensations, drowsiness, and laziness can be looked upon as cousins of tired feelings. To continue that comparison, despair is the big brother of tired feelings. A few psychologists, however, regard despair as possibly the emotion that accompanies tired feelings.

Despair and tiredness have about the same causes, though tired feelings appear to be aroused by lesser causes. Both have about the same effects on a person's behavior and feelings, and they often occur together so it is almost impossible to tell one from the other. We can understand the essential quality and overwhelming force of tired feelings better if we look into despair at this point.

The most meaningful report on the inner nature of despair has come from Dr. Raymond B. Cattell's factor analysis of the basic qualities in human personality, and of the inner forces which motivate people. He reports that despair is touched off when an individual comes up against some frustrating situation which (a) prevents him from reaching some goal he earnestly hoped to attain, and (b) which he is powerless to change. With the death of his beloved Ann Rutledge, for example, Lincoln was plunged into weeks of despair and tiredness.

Frustrating, or restricting, situations are common in business, and probably have most impact on the ambitious person. After he gets so far up the ladder, it may dawn on him that he has become a specialist in a blind alley and that he is too old to start over on a ladder that goes higher. Tired feelings are consequently rather common in middle-aged executives who have become staff specialists.

What we have been calling a restricting situation is one which limits a person and which he cannot change appreciably. He is stuck with it, or in it. An example is being held to standard procedures on a routine job, or, on the home front, being trapped, as the housewife describes it, by taking care of children and getting meals—the common result is "housewife's fatigue." Labor-saving conveniences do not alter the critical parts of the frustrating situation.

Personality clashes, also, limit the person and he is usually powerless to change the other person. In addition, the clash often brings out an attitude of hostility—"do me a favor and drop dead"—which adds another complication (a feeling of guilt) to the resulting tired feelings.

2. Other reactions to frustrating situations

Such frustrating situations may arouse other reactions than despair or tired feelings. What the reaction will be depends upon the inner self of the person involved. Dr. Cattell pointed out three other reactions we should note.

Trying to escape the frustrating situation is one. Escape may be sought by looking for a different job, or the house-wife may hire a baby-sitter and take an office job. Usually, however, when planning how to escape the trap a great deal of anxiety is aroused, because of the risks a change would involve. If he doesn't escape successfully, the anxiety may become so intense that it adds greatly to his tiredness.

Wanting to escape is widespread. In studies of men who worked on an assembly line, C. R. Walker and R. H. Guest learned that a large share had considered changing to work that was not as restrictive. The big lure was to set up a small repair business of their own; but anxiety about the risks of making good on their own kept most of them from taking that step. "The American Dream" seems to be to have an independent career, but for the majority it will have to remain a dream.

Owning an automobile is a way many escape from some of the daily restrictions. Depending upon the bus is restrictive; one can't go and come at will, but is chained to a timetable and fixed routes. Although owning cars may keep them anxiously in debt—so that they are "working mostly to pay installments"—they are willing to do it because it is the only way many have to be independent in their goings and comings. So the average employee has to spend one full day's pay each week to run his own automobile. And three out of four families in the U.S. own an automobile, while one family out of six owns two.

Becoming pugnacious (hostile) is another way some people try to get the better of a restricting situation. They may destroy property, or merely sulk like a teen-ager. It is suspected that this way causes a large share of the voluntary holding down of output. It is also probably an element in

From booklet "Growing Pains." Courtesy
The Connecticut Mutual Life Insurance Co.

Contrariness, or negativism, instead of tired feelings, may be the chief reaction to a situation which the person responds to as if it were restrictive

some of the unreasonable demands for fringe benefits, and in the formation of societies that are against this or that.

Daydreaming that the quandary is solved is the fourth way of reacting to such constraining situations. The person daydreams that he is up the ladder where he hoped to be. Or that she is not actually a household drudge but a royal princess in disguise, and that a prince from Bonaco is coming to take her out of the restricting situation. This way is rather common among workers on repetitive, monotonous jobs; their delightful daydreams make the jobs enjoyable, but cut into quality and increase accidents or errors.

3. The yearning for sympathetic help

The keynote of the despair way of reacting is that those who react thus become defeatist, and think it futile to try. With loss of hope, they become daunted rather than dauntless. They are deterred from trying and become strongly inclined to be inactive; glands and nerves shift the balance to energy-saving, and the persons feel "too tired to do anything." They also tend to become depressed, or at least discouraged and gloomy. This is particularly the case with older people, and it sometimes ends up as melancholia with them.

We have previously noted the close association of depressed moods with tired feelings. This occurs even with "artificial depression" produced by drugs, as is shown in the chartoon. Both curves are for healthy Air Force men who spent several hours relaxing in an air-conditioned lounge. The upper curve pictures the slight increase in tiredness as time went on when no drug had been taken. The lower (more tired) curve is for equally healthy men who took a depressant pill at 9:30. By the time the pill took effect, these men felt more tired and that state of feeling persisted for about three hours, after which the effects of the pill wore off.

The person who is trapped in restrictive situations and becomes depressed or tired as a result, yearns acutely for sympathetic help. Not maudlin sympathy and unrealistic encouragement, but sound counsel which will show him how to do something to change or master the situation. He may seek help from the personnel office, or a minister, or a bartender, or by eagerly reading a "success" book which builds hopes which are likely to plunge him into more despair when they are not achieved. He would get the most skilled help from a suitably trained psychologist or psychiatrist.

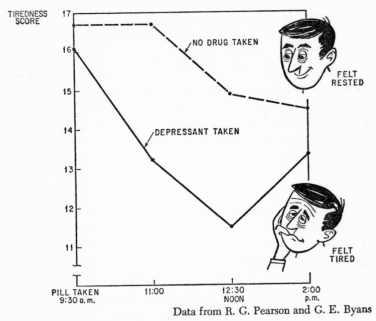

Data from R. G. Pearson and G. E. Byans

A depressant pill made them feel tired although they had done no work

Reasonable and understanding help may lead the person out of his despair and into reasonable hope which will stimulate him to rise and try again—as Lincoln did, many times. Lincoln was fortunate in getting sympathetic help from his friends and neighbors which enabled him to adjust to the thorny parts of life. He was unfortunate, however, in not receiving it from his wife, who nagged him while others gave friendly counsel. This nagging might have instigated a personality clash, but apparently Lincoln did not react to it in that way, at least not critically—it was just something he put up with, and if he felt sorry for himself on this score, he gallantly said nothing about it.

The story of Fred N., the government executive in Chapter 5, and of Ruth B., the widow who married the banker in Chapter 9, illustrate the usefulness of sympathetic help.

When there is reasonable hope of reaching one's goals, there should be fewer tired feelings along the way there. The individual should consider this when setting his personal goals, and when choosing a career. The employer should consider it in every phase of his establishment if he expects his employees to have tireless zest for their work.

4. Tired feelings cool off the will to work

What is most distinctive about tired feelings is that they overpower, or replace, the will to work. This probably arises from the age-old reaction of resting when the organism is threatened by overwork or disease. The central feature of the tired feeling is an aversion to do things because of an "all-goneness" that prevents the person from pulling himself together enough to work.

Other things will weaken the will to work, of course, such as pugnacity which is expressed by holding down output. In the case of tired feelings, however, the will to work is put into cold storage *in*voluntarily. The person would like to thaw it out but is unable to as long as nerves and glands tilt the balance to conserve energy which does not need to be conserved.

The deep aversion to action when feeling tired is sometimes toward one task only; shift to more interesting work and the tiredness vanishes.

But in most instances the aversion to activity spreads to almost all actions and cuts a wide swath in limiting the person's behavior; it may inhibit the person from shifting to work he knows would be interesting. It often extends to an aversion to trying anything new, regardless of how easy it might be. Tired people resist change and cling to familiar ways, shown interestingly by "the same tune keeps running through my head." Dr. J. W. Dunlap has found that this impulse to cling to the familiar when tired is also shown by tired people reverting to the less efficient work methods they had used when learning the job.

Sadly, this aversion to trying something new also keeps some tired people from following the sympathetic help they crave; just can't bring themselves to climb out of the familiar rut.

5. "Too tired to eat ... or to talk."

When tired feelings are marked the aversion to visible activity is likely to spread even to things that are enjoyable and almost instinctive in character. Drs. Raymond B. Cattell and Lester B. Luborsky found that interest in both food and sex dwindled when people felt tired.

"Too tired to eat" is a fact that illustrates clearly the force and wide swath of tired feelings. Almost everyone has noticed this in himself following some strenuous visible activity. Sir Winston Churchill took personal measures against this during World War II by lying down to rest before dinner.

When a person has chronic tired feelings he is also likely to have chronic lack of appetite, and may lose weight. Such

loss of weight is sometimes wrongly interpreted as a sign
that he has been "working too hard." This was illustrated by
Gerald N., a twenty-four-year-old accounting student who
was given sympathetic help by Dr. Henry P. Laughlin.
Gerald's mother insisted that he study accounting, although
that was the last thing in the world he wanted to do. Clearly
a restrictive situation. He had made a good record in
preparatory school. "When I was there," he said, "I was
interested and liked what I was doing. I was spry and full
of pep. Now I can hardly drag myself around. I feel tired
and don't want to do much." Along with the persistent
tired feelings, he lost appetite. During the first six months in
accounting school he lost thirty-two pounds because he did
not eat.

"I began to feel 'filled up' inside, and my appetite went
away," he said. "I would be hungry in the morning, but after
working in the classes awhile I would get a bloated feeling.
I was never hungry during work or after finishing it. I felt
better week ends, but I dreaded even the thought of going
back to accounting on Monday. As Monday came closer, I
noticed the 'filled up' feeling was stronger."

When Dr. O. G. Edholm measured appetite in military
cadets, he found that on the day they had been given a really
energy-depleting workout, they ate considerably less food
than usual, although they needed more than usual. After a
couple of days, however, when the cadets were over their
tired feelings from the hard workout, they ate enough
extra to make up for their previously poor appetites.

The person who comes home "too tired to talk" provides
another example of how the tired feelings stifle the will to
engage in any activity. Dr. Haverland's tests showed that
verbal ability was lowered when tired feelings were high.

There are other phenomena which often go with tired

feelings, and which tend to reinforce the inclination to be inactive. Examples are the feeling of being drugged, or sluggish, or of general discomfort, which may lead the person to imagine "something is wrong with my system." Usually what is wrong with his system is some autonomic and glandular responses to clashes or restrictions.

Feeling tired is, in many ways, the opposite of feeling fit to work, though usually one is fit for work except for one's tired feelings.

Feeling tired can also be looked upon as the opposite of warming up to work. You cool off for work when tired, though most times you actually have energy to spare.

Why do these feelings change during the day, and during the week? Why do some of them come over us suddenly, others gradually? Those are some of the questions for the next chapter.

CHAPTER 13

The steps from peppy to tired

1. Tiring out during the day

How quickly should a person become tired?

It depends upon many factors, of course. The speed with which tired feelings come over one may give useful hints about the causes.

A slow but steady increase occurs when physical work is being done. The increase is faster if the person has sedentary habits, or has not been used to the particular work. The sedentary person pays a price for taking things easy most of the time. One reason is that his blood has "become lazy" and does not carry the oxygen it might. (See the chartoon in Chapter 15.)

105

There is also a slight increase in tired feelings as the day goes on, whether the person does physical work or not. Just being up and awake seems to become tiring after so long.

The upper curve in the chartoon shows how tired feelings

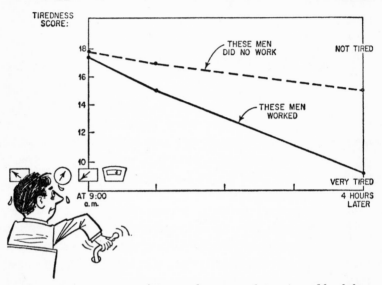

Work was continuous use of 3 controls so as to bring 4 steadily shifting pointers back to zero

Data from R. G. Pearson and G. E. Byars

They tired a little without working (But the demanding work tired them more)

become slightly stronger even when a person does no work. The men who worked at taxing work, but which did not require much energy expenditure, tired out considerably more, as shown in the lower curve.

Why should doing no work cause tired feelings to increase? Perhaps because having to kill time becomes monotonous (a restriction), except for the few persons who have a dependent character make-up and who enjoy killing time.

It seems to be the normal course of events for one to become more tired as the day goes on, whether one works or not. With a very few persons, however, this usual course is reversed; some kinds of nervous people are more tired in the morning than afternoon, and after dark feel their freshest.

2. *More tired from day to day*

A slow but steady increase in tiredness from one day to the next sometimes takes place when the person keeps at really strenuous work that tends to use up his energy supply. The same result may occur when he does not have adequate food, as happened in concentration camps. This is not seen much nowadays in industrialized countries because machinery does most of the hard work, and there is more food than needed.

When the tired feelings increase from day to day at present it is more likely to be because of some disease or unbalanced physical condition. The tired feelings associated with anemia, or undulant fever, for example, creep up at a snail's pace, more or less in step with the advance of the disease. Glandular conditions, such as Napoleon's failing pituitary, or thyroid disturbances which are more common, or the gland changes at adolescence and the change of life which everyone has, have similar effects in bringing on "creeping tiredness."

There is also a tendency for the tired feelings to become worse from day to day as work loses its challenge and becomes boresome. This was shown by Dr. Haverland's tests; as time went on the man became more bored by the day-after-day sameness of the work he had to do.

This may be a reason why experienced employees are

subject to tired feelings after their work has become easy routine. It also occurs with many people upon retirement; after a few weeks, "having to play" becomes restrictive and tiresome, as the illustration dramatizes.

When the tired feelings are associated with depressed

Loafing can be tiring. This unhappy man demonstrates what many surveys bring out: the desire for money alone is not why successful businessmen keep on working.

Study this scene. His wife finally persuaded him to quit work and enjoy his money. Reluctantly he agreed to try it.

Looks like the life of Riley, doesn't it? But think a minute. This man was a business success because he felt a glow of accomplishment as he went along. He was creating more than financial security. His work added substance to his life.

Now he wishes he was back on the job. His life is aimless. He doesn't know what to do with himself. One day is like another. He feels restless and listless. This captain of industry was not cut out to be a private among the ranks of loafers.

From the booklet "Satisfaction Guaranteed." **Courtesy** The Connecticut Mutual Life Insurance Co.

moods, or despair, they are more likely to become stronger as the first few days pass. After a week—or perhaps not until a month—they gradually ease up. The tiredness in these instances is also likely to be more severe in the mornings than afternoons, reversing the usual daily course.

3. Sudden tired feelings

Other tired feelings come with a rush—and may leave with a rush.

Some teen-agers suddenly lose their pep and feel all worn out when ordered to do some chore—"taking the fun out of life." But as soon as the chore is finished—or evaded— they have lots of pep for doing what the chore restricted them from doing.

Something similar frequently happens to the teen-ager's father or mother. Doing housework provides a good example. The chartoon shows how two women felt tired while doing the weekly two-hour stint of cleaning their own houses. It was not heavy, energy-consuming work. Let's picture why one woman became much more tired than the other, and why she suddenly did not feel tired after working more than an hour.

Mrs. N. is the woman who obviously did not like the cleaning job; some parts she liked even less than others. After the first half hour of general picking up and getting the work equipment together she reported much tiredness. Then she started to use the vacuum cleaner, which she hated because of its noise, the way the hose and cord interfered with her freedom of movement. She felt it was generally restrictive. So her tired feelings went up to a peak. When she turned to dusting, however, after 90 minutes of the cleaning work, she felt little tiredness. She "got her energy back" as soon as she started dusting; that was work she enjoyed and she could sing while she worked. An example of the way changing to another task usually rests a person, provided they change to a task they like. (William Gladstone changed to the hard task of chopping wood to "rest up!")

Let's look at Mrs. T. on the chart for a moment. She was purring along smoothly all through her weekly cleaning. A

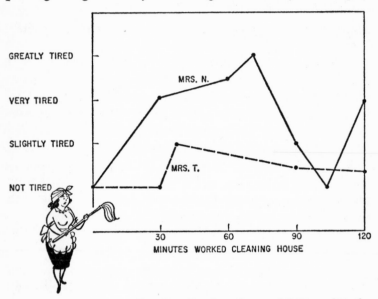

Data from Drs. Irma Gross and S. Howard Bartley

Why did brief housecleaning make one woman feel so much more tired out?

happy housewife who did not seem to hate the vacuum cleaner. No disliked tasks to bring on a sudden rush of tired feelings. Lucky woman—she could sing all the time. It is a pretty safe bet, too, that she did a more thorough cleaning job than Mrs. N.

Tired feelings frequently come with a rush from personality clashes. One executive always had a sudden tired spell whenever he had to confer with a colleague who he suspected was trying to undermine his reputation with the higher-ups.

When something restrictive comes along in the work, there may be a sudden tired feeling. One machine worker began to have tired spells whenever he had to go to the tool crib, because the new rules restricted him from selecting or sharpening the tool himself.

The tired feelings associated with an allergic condition may come on suddenly, especially when the allergy is to some food that is eaten only occasionally but in large quantity. A young contractor had sudden tiredness after taking beer and peanuts—and he usually took them together in good quantity. These tired feelings remain steady when the food, or dust, or pollen is present all the time.

As a rule, however, the first thing to suspect when the tired feeling is sudden is that some personality clash or restrictiveness has touched a sensitive spot and thereby upset the balance in nerves and glands.

4. What part of you feels tired?

Once in a while we can locate exactly where we feel tired, but these times are rare. This is usually only after we have overused, or abused, some muscle which begins to feel sore—after shoveling snow, for instance, or after playing too hard on the first day of vacation.

Blue-collar workers can often locate where they feel tired. A few white-collar workers can, as we learned in Chapter 11 about why typists felt tired in their necks rather than in their fingers which did the work.

In those few instances when we can tell just where we feel tired, muscle sensations (or soreness) probably constitute a large part of the mixture we call feeling tired. When there are no special muscle sensations, or soreness, we tend to feel tired all over.

And almost always the tired feelings are felt all over. They permeate every part and affect the entire person. This is to be expected, for we have seen in Chapter 7 that the autonomics can either step on the gas or on the brakes for every organ and involuntary muscle in the body (except the sweat glands).

The all-over feeling of tiredness is more of a hindrance in getting things done than are the few tired (or sore) feelings we can clearly locate in, say, legs or shoulders. When only the legs feel tired, or sore, we can still work with hands or head. But when we feel "all pooped out," we lose the motivation to do anything except sit and rest. This was often Lincoln's predicament, and at those times he would sit all day with his feet on the table, or lie stretched out on the floor for hours, gazing at the ceiling.

5. Tired all over, all the time

Tired feelings usually come and go. But a few people feel tired all over, all the time, and have been figuratively described as "born tired."

Charles Darwin had tired feelings all day every day, but not until after he was about twenty-five. From then on, every morning he woke up tired and did not feel fit for work all day, whether he spent the day in rest or at work.

In his times not much was known, or even suspected, about the part personal difficulties—clashes and restrictive-ness—play in such chronic tired conditions. But he learned to master his tired feelings by doggedly working, even on Sundays, whether he felt like it or not—and he never felt like it.

Darwin made himself a producer in spite of lasting tiredness. The work to which he was dedicated seemed to be the best antidote to help him forget his tired feelings. This is worth noting because specialists believe that if more moderns were dedicated to their work there would be fewer tired feelings.

In contrast with Darwin, many chronically tired people give in to their tired feelings. Dr. James A. Hadfield reported about a woman so tired that she regularly slept from 9 P.M. to 7 A.M., but always woke up tired—so tired that she had to rest a while to "gather up enough strength" to nibble at breakfast. She was too tired to eat and the "work" of nibbling tired her out so much more that she had to go back to bed and rest until time for the next meal.

All that resting only made her softer and more susceptible to tiring on the slightest exertion. In most such instances rest does not reduce the pestering tiredness, nor increase energy. There are times when we should give in and rest, but usually the better way to keep the tired feelings from becoming oversize is to follow Darwin's example. Work anyway.

6. A scale for sizing up tired feelings

Feeling tired is the opposite of feeling fit for the work at hand. When we don't feel fresh and peppy, we feel more or less tired. To size up our tired feelings, therefore, we have to think in terms of a scale which has tired feelings as the anchor at one end and energetic feelings anchoring the other end.

One of the first scales to be devised on this basis was developed at the School of Aviation Medicine of the U.S. Air Force. There Dr. Richard G. Pearson, a research psychologist, used modern psychometric methods to produce checklists which could be used to find how tired a person felt.

A simplified version of one of his scales is given in the diagram—a simple scale for a complex state of feeling. Each of the steps measures about the same size difference in feeling tired, or feeling peppy. The difference between steps 8 and 9, for instance, is about as great as between any other two adjoining steps.

The neutral, or dividing point, is at step 5—"Not too tired...Not too fresh." That is about where we would

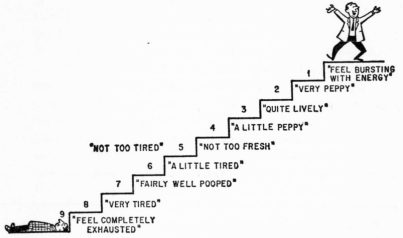

1 "FEEL BURSTING WITH ENERGY"
2 "VERY PEPPY"
3 "QUITE LIVELY"
4 "A LITTLE PEPPY"
"NOT TOO TIRED"   5 "NOT TOO FRESH"
6 "A LITTLE TIRED"
7 "FAIRLY WELL POOPED"
8 "VERY TIRED"
9 "FEEL COMPLETELY EXHAUSTED"

Adapted from R. G. Pearson and G. E. Byars

How tired do you feel at present? (A nine-step scale for tired feelings)

expect most people to check themselves when nothing had happened to make them feel tired; no strong urge to rest, and at the same time no strong urge to be up and doing. As we go below that neutral point, the tired feelings become stronger with each step down.

About the only time we can honestly check step 9 is after severe exertion, such as mountain climbing—"ready to drop in my tracks." And about the only time we can honestly check step 1 is when we are full of pep pills, or in a manic condition (the opposite of depression) and have to "hold back" to keep from overdoing.

You probably know some people who would be described as hovering around step 4, "A little peppy," most of the time. An example is provided by President Theodore Roosevelt who hovered around steps 3 and 4. When he went down to step 5—"Not too tired . . . Not too fresh"—it was tiredness for him.

Other people characteristically hover around lower steps on the scale. Lincoln, for example, was at steps 6 or 7 most of the time, and occasionally went down to 8 or even 9.

Those two Presidents illustrate individual differences in what psychologists call surgency. Roosevelt was a surgent person; Lincoln was desurgent.

Such individual differences in a person's level of tired-or-peppy are probably due to two general conditions. One is the way his autonomics and endocrines function, and this is considered largely inborn, although ailments may modify them. The other general condition is the inner self which the person has acquired, largely accidentally and early in life, as his habitual way of meeting life.

The end result is that feeling tired is a relative matter from person to person. Roosevelt would be tired, for him, at step 5, but Lincoln would be rested, for him, at the same step.

Whatever a person's characteristic level, it is likely to go down a step the last hour of the forenoon, and again the last hour of work in the afternoon. For some puzzling reason, many people are a step lower on Mondays than on other days of the week; one explanation is that they hate to start another week of restricted activity on the job.

It is also likely to go down a step on hot days, or in an overheated room, or during the hot season of the year. Conversely, on chilly days it usually goes up a step. The warmer environment makes it more difficult for the body to maintain its steady state.

From twenty to forty years of age people tend to be at their highest (least tired) on such a scale. After about fifty they generally come down about a step every ten or so years. The complex machinery that adjusts the steady state does not do as good a job when it is not as young as it used to be.

Numerous other factors affect the level one way or another. Many of these have been mentioned. In the remainder of this book we will refresh and extend our knowledge of these, and wrap the various practical points into packages that can conveniently be carried in the head.

Our next foray will be a look into the lives of three distinguished personages whose problems with their tired feelings have some instructive messages for us. First we will learn about Justice Oliver Wendell Holmes, who usually hovered around steps 5 and 6, but who could suddenly be plunged down to step 8.

CHAPTER 14

Justice Holmes's right to feel tired

1. How clashes made the future justice tired

More things than meet the eye make people tired. This was clearly illustrated in the life of Justice Oliver Wendell Holmes, who served on the U.S. Supreme Court for thirty years. There was no backbreaking labor, or poor health, to make him feel tired. Yet as he was striving to get on in his profession he had his tired spells because he was trapped in two tiring situations. One was clashing personalities, the other a restrictive work situation.

As a bachelor attorney living with his parents in their tall brick Boston home, he would often be overtaken by tired feelings in the middle of a meal. Sometimes he became too tired to finish, and would climb to his rooms on the third floor to rest. This mealtime tiredness occurred only when his father was at the table.

Father and son were similar in having a good supply of brains. In other respects they were almost as opposite as people can be. Even in appearance; the father was a short five feet five inches and quick moving, the son six feet three inches and slow moving. The father was surgent, egotistical, and vain, which he blandly admitted with a touch of bragging; he was also bossy and a show off. The son was desurgent, retiring, eager to study and to think, minding his own business.

Mealtime brought out the father's traits in all their glory. At the table he was a talkative autocrat, chattering, showing off, and bragging endlessly.

Dinner guests thought the father a brilliant conversationalist—so did the father. Guests were invigorated by his witticisms—so was the father. He invited a procession of guests so he could parade his titillating talk and recite his latest topical verse.

But the studious and reflective son could not view his father's flow of words with the same detachment the visitors showed. The guests heard it only occasionally; the son had to put up with it every meal. A thinker rather than a talker, he was profoundly bored, and on occasions downright annoyed, by the monologue on topics he considered petty. To the son it was nonstop yackety-yak.

Anyway, the son had strong hostile attitudes toward his domineering father. A shadow would cross his face when his father came into the same room. Most things the lively and bossy father did were irritating, or frustrating, to the future justice. He had to hold himself in check when his father was near. It all gave him queasy feelings.

These personality clashes caught the son in a distressing conflict within his own impulses. When his father wore out the son's patience (which was quickly done), there was an impulse to tell his father to shut up; but his gentlemanly impulses tugged against it.

Such conflicts—inner tugs of war—have great power in building up tired feelings. The strain of restraining oneself can bring on tired feelings much sooner than physical labor does. In addition, the tired feelings arising from friction with other personalities tend to be especially disturbing because a feeling of guilt, or of anxiety, or both, is often mixed in with the tired feeling itself.

2. Clashes in the modern world

The collision of personalities does not have to be violent to leave tired feelings in its wake. There can be sufficient clash without an open argument or back talk or spoken criticism. Onlookers may not be aware of the friction.

Even one of the clashing personalities may not notice a head-on collision, as self-confident Dr. Holmes seemed blithely ignorant of the friction he caused his son and which the son felt so acutely that it almost knocked him out at times.

As a result, clash situations can be insidious and are much more common than most people realize. Parents and bosses are often the focal points of clashes without knowing it. So they wonder: "What's the matter with my child (or my workers) that makes them get tired when they shouldn't?" If they only knew, the child or worker has good reason for feeling tired.

Much of the tiredness felt by teen-agers—and they have more than their fair share of it—is probably due to clashes right in the home between personalities that are out of harmony. The consequent conflicts in impulses and attitudes toward the other person, and toward oneself, make many teen-agers mixed-up and tired out. The youth is seldom actually lazy, or in poor health, as his parents may fear. He is more likely made tired by the annoyance, boredom, and perhaps hostility generated in his interpersonal relations with his perplexed parents.

From the booklet "The Worry-Go-Round." Courtesy The Connecticut Mutual Life Insurance Co.

When clashing personalities come together at the dining table, the clashes often become stronger. This is another aspect, too, of "too tired to eat."

Sometimes, of course, the parent is also worn down in these struggles between clashing personalities with divergent hopes. Parents, being more mature and experienced, should be better able than the teen-ager to forbear and tolerate the clash situations. Should be able to, but often are not.

That is why life begins at forty for some parents, when their children leave the parental nest and thus change this situation, to the relief of everybody concerned—including the neighbors.

When a parent says: "It's time for Effie to get married," or "George should take that good job on the Coast," he may really mean: "He makes me tired and I'll never feel rested until he is not here to clash with me."

In business, too, it is often collisions in interpersonal relations rather than the work itself that brings on tired feelings. It may be personality clashes between the boss and a worker; for a very few bosses it is with all their workers. It may be between workers who rub each other the wrong way. It may be with customers—the strain of being agreeable to disagreeable people for which salespeople are paid.

The men at the top, as well as on the assembly line, get caught in situations where personalities may clash. It has been observed, however, that the men at the top are more likely to be able to tolerate personalities that conflict with them—a quality that can help them in more ways than one to get closer to the top.

Are people today more likely to be caught in personality clashes than their grandparents were? Convincing arguments have been made that people are now exposed to more opportunities *not* to get along with others, while at the same time the need for getting along has increased. If true, this is both ends working against the middle.

No doubt conditions of living and working have changed during the last century so that "togetherness" is more necessary today. David Riesman describes in his book *The Lonely Crowd* how this has greatly modified people's attitudes;

many try hard to be popular and get along, and some suc-
ceed at it.

Nowadays, for instance, most of us have to work for
others, or with others. Independence at work is almost an
historical curiosity. This would not be bad so far as tired
feelings go, but for the fact that it is necessary to compete
with other people for jobs and for promotions. This puts a
premium on aggressiveness, and aggressiveness is a potent
cause of clashes.

It would also not be bad if we could always work with
the sort of people we would choose as "my kind of person."
It is usually the boss, however, who decides who works
with whom. A large share of people have to work with job
mates who would not be even their second or third choices,
if they had a chance to choose. They may work together side
by side, but that is the extent of their togetherness.

Another trend cited as possibly making clashes more
difficult to avoid is smaller houses and apartments than in
the past. When two people in the same household clash, it
is now seldom possible for them to avoid each other, the
way Holmes took refuge in his third-floor quarters in his
father's large house. Today the criticized teen-ager seeks
refuge at a teen-agers' hangout, the irritated father retreats
to his lodge or tavern, the disparaged mother nurses her
wounds in the soft light of a romantic movie. "Apartness"
sometimes helps people escape from clashes when "togetherness" has failed.

Mention should also be made of our increasing mobility.
More people move more than a century ago. On the average,
they move to a new job every three and a half years, to a
new city or neighborhood every five years. Each move con-
fronts them with new sets of significant people they have to
get along with. And often the moves have been made largely

to get away from significant people with whom they clash. Thus a move may be a jump from one frying pan into another so far as clashes are concerned. Some people try to solve this dilemma by keeping away from neighbors or fellow workers.

"He makes me tired!" thus turns out to be more than a picturesque expression. Unsatisfying relationships with other people create stressful situations which cause many otherwise unexplainable spells of tiredness. Such spells are distressing, not only because we may feel guilty about our attitudes toward the irritating person, but also because we can't understand why we feel tired. The mystery of why we are tired can feed our anxiety, in a vicious circle.

The clashing person does not have to be present to touch off tired feelings. The mere thought of how he annoys us can be enough to bring on tiredness—out of sight is not out of mind in this instance. Or, a tired spell can be touched off by seeing a stranger who in some way reminds us of a person who sets us on edge—more mystery to worry the puzzled person who does not understand that it is usually something other than hard work that causes the tired feelings.

In general, we can say that people who do not get along well with each other, or who have widely differing interests and viewpoints, are likely to be tiring to one, or the other, or to both of them. The one who gets tired is the one who is unable to tolerate people who are "not my kind," or who has touchy spots in his inner self.

> We have a right to feel tired when we clash, secretly or openly, with another person.... But we also have the right to learn to tolerate "fools," if not gladly, at least well enough to lessen tired feelings.... While we can't always evade

clashes, we can at least become a bit immune to them and put up with what has to be put up with.

3. How restrictive work made Attorney Holmes tired

Soon after Holmes was married he and his bride fled the parental nest for light-housekeeping rooms above a drugstore. They ate most of their meals around the corner at the Parker House. The lanky son no longer had to stop in the middle of a meal because of tired feelings.

But shortly he began to feel tired during his working hours in the office on Court Street. Why should light office work tire a man who took to the law as if it were second nature for him? The cut-and-dried legal processes quickly became routine for his active mind and were soon boring to him. As boring as his father's repetitive witticisms before each new crop of dinner guests.

Then there was the dirty work, as he thought it, of helping greedy clients in their grudge fights. He was an idealist who had little stomach for that phase of law practice. To him it was futile, and at times disgusting, Catherine D. Bowen reported. Merely a way to make a living while his heart and hopes were elsewhere—restrictive.

His heart was on clarifying some aspects of law which he considered basic. This was more important, he felt, than collecting overdue debts or gathering evidence about boundary lines. If he could only work on the basic law, he would feel he was getting somewhere, that he was working for himself rather than untangling others from messes their greed had gotten them into. Unfortunately, he had to make a living or move back to his father's table. He was trapped in restrictive work.

As human as the next person, Holmes became tired out

by the easy tasks of the law office because, to him, his work situation was restrictive and cramped his hopes. His partners might feel some challenge about collecting an overdue debt, but to Holmes it was humdrum. He yearned to extend himself, to put his wits to work, and do something to clarify the basic philosophy of The Law.

He was in a fix similar to that of modern factory and office workers who perform easy cut-and-dried tasks in the prescribed ways, who get pay raises in due course, but who are restricted from deciding what to do or how to do it. They are tired out less by what they do on the job than by their feeling of being restricted from doing something else, or doing the task differently. More about this in the next Chapter.

4. He found a way out

Holmes found a way out for himself by leading a double life. He began to work evenings on his quest for an understanding of the common law. Now he was working for himself, after hours at least, and not on grudge fights and wills. He left money grubbing at the office. At home he worked at his self-chosen and self-planned quest of analyzing the experience of the world which gives life to The Law.

Now as he walked late afternoons from the office to his apartment, the tired feelings that had plagued him at the office dropped away. His long-strided walk seemed to grow more energetic with each step, unlike his slow walk to Court Street mornings.

Nearly ten years of this double life of working late at night on *his* quest passed. He lost weight, but felt invigorated with zest and satisfaction. His friend William James, first psychologist at Harvard, noted that Holmes had become a changed man.

In like manner, some factory and office workers are reborn when they discover some engrossing after-hours personal quest to give them a new lease on their hopes, hopes which are perhaps cramped by routine work planned by an industrial engineer whose objective is to save time and mo-

One way out of a restrictive situation. Even if you wanted to, you couldn't buy this chair at any price. It may not look like much to you. But to its proud owner, it's a thing of beauty.

Our happy carpenter is a lawyer during the day. When he gets home, he can hardly wait to get down into his workroom. But if you think the hours of toil, the bruised fingers and broken fingernails, add up to drudgery for Oscar, you're badly mistaken.

The hours spent making this monstrosity were happy, creative hours. "There's a little of Oscar in every inch of that chair," his understanding wife tells her friends.

Work? Of course. Plenty of it. What a stimulating sense of accomplishment results! There's nothing like it.

From the booklet "Satisfaction Guaranteed." Courtesy The Connecticut Mutual Life Insurance Co.

tions rather than to stimulate zestful self-development and personal growth of the worker.

At forty, life began again for Holmes. That year his little book *The Common Law* appeared; the fruit of his ten-year double life, it freed the common law from dogmatic abstractions and made an international reputation for him. It also freed Holmes himself from the cut-and-dried drudgery, to him, of the office, as it led him to a bench on the state Supreme Court. There he began to hit his stride.

Nor did Holmes stop his after-hours double life. He kept up zest-bringing quests throughout his long life. When President Franklin D. Roosevelt called on the aging justice to honor his birthday, he found the ninety-year-old sage reading Greek. "To improve my mind," was the explanation. Still growing!

> We have a right to feel tired when we make a living at work in which the tasks are cut-and-dried, and in which our growth and self-direction are restricted.... But we also have a right to develop additional skills so we can grow into more completely satisfying work which, though it may be harder, will probably be tackled with attitudes which will make it less tiring.... And the employer can usually reduce tiredness in his workers best by providing for more self-direction and personal growth.

CHAPTER 15

How we have become vulnerable to feeling tired

---

1. ONE PRICE OF PROGRESS
2. SEDENTARY PEOPLE ARE VULNERABLE
3. PEOPLE WITH BOSSES ARE VULNERABLE
4. ORGANIZATION MEN ARE VULNERABLE

1. One price of progress

People are built so that a great number of things can make them feel tired. In the remote past these feelings probably had survival value. But in our modern civilization too many people feel too tired too much of the time, and their tired feelings are more likely to have nuisance value than survival value.

You will recall that one city man out of five told Dr. Robert L. Thorndike that he tired easily.

Housewives, too. Drs. Irma Gross and S. Howard Bartley

studied housewives who were doing two-hour cleaning jobs in their own homes. Nearly one third of the women became greatly tired. Some of the women tired out after only a half hour, but "got their energy back" and did not feel as tired after working an hour longer. (Look again at the chartoon in Chapter 13.)

One-fourth of these women reported scarcely any tired feelings while doing the cleaning. These were the ones who did the better work. That is not surprising, because tired feelings usually cause people to cut corners and skip details.

In addition, a sizable share of people feel all tired out when they get up after a full night's sleep—tired even before they start work. Dr. Nathaniel Kleitman found that the average white-collar person felt tired on getting up about half of the mornings. A few felt tired three mornings out of four. Dr. Thorndike's records showed that about one out of five men woke up tired on most mornings.

It was much the same story with aviation cadets who were in the prime of life and were doing light work. Dr. William Neufeld found that only one out of four woke up feeling rested. Three out of four always, or sometimes, felt tired on getting up mornings.

The prevalence of tired feelings is also indicated by the reasons people go to a physician's office, or clinic. Some 10 to 30 per cent of the patients go because they are bothered by tired feelings which they can't bear in peace any longer. We saw in Chapter 2 that in only one fourth of these was anything wrong with the body to account for the chronic tiredness.

What causes all these tired feelings that are not due to diseases or strenuous work? Probably progress—a price paid for the progress of civilization. There are no figures available for earlier centuries, but authorities are strongly of the opinion that tired feelings are now more prevalent. This is because civilization has changed in some ways that make more people live and work under conditions which bring on tired feelings that are associated with invisible activity.

Sir Heneage Ogilvie, the British surgeon and author of the book *No Miracles among Friends,* summed it up this way:

"We make a great mistake if we think that happiness consists in having a forty-hour week, a smart car, a television set, and a chromium-plated bathroom.

"Happiness consists in (a) a job that provides a succession of varied and interesting tasks (b) that demand skill (c) and call for individual enterprise, (d) that is useful to the community in which we live, (e) that offers security if we do it conscientiously (f) and advancement if we do it well, (g) and if not a belief in a future life, at any rate a confident belief in the future that this life holds for us.

"All these things the craftsmen and peasants of the Middle Ages had. All, or nearly all of them we lack today."

You can bring these points home by asking these questions to find whether these seven things are provided in your own life:

(a) Does your job give you varied and interesting tasks?
(b) Does it demand skill?
(c) Can you use your own initiative in working it out?
(d) Is your work useful to your neighbors?
(e) Is it steady work, with no layoffs?
(f) Are increased earnings and promotion in store for you?
(g) Are you optimistic about the future in general?

Questions answered "No" indicate possible reasons for being vulnerable to tired feelings. And in modern industrial civilizations the majority of workers would doubtless have a majority of "No" answers. Further comment unnecessary.

2. Sedentary people are vulnerable

A century ago most men, and many women, had to do heavy work, every day. But machines have gradually taken over most of the backbreaking work, as well as much that wouldn't strain a gnat's back.

Completely contrary to what might be expected, sedentary

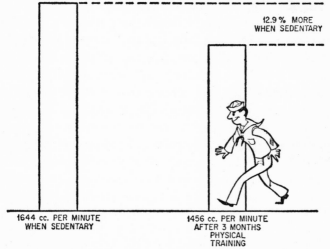

12.9% MORE
WHEN SEDENTARY

1644 cc. PER MINUTE
WHEN SEDENTARY

1456 cc. PER MINUTE
AFTER 3 MONTHS
PHYSICAL
TRAINING

Data from Dr. Gordon N. French

They used more oxygen while walking when in a sedentary condition

work increases the susceptibility to tired feelings. This is because easy work, or too much resting or sitting, allows the body processes to settle into a sluggish steady state that sets the stage for tired rather than for peppy feelings.

As an example we can consider the body's capacity to use oxygen, which we learned in Chapter 6 is the chief bottleneck when doing strenuous visible activity. The chartoon pictures what happened to the capacity to use oxygen when healthy young men were brought out of their sedentary condition by three months of systematic physical training at the U.S. Naval School of Aviation Medicine. When walking at a rate of four miles an hour—moderately light visible activity—they used nearly 13 per cent more oxygen when they were in a sedentary condition. They would have tired much sooner from oxygen shortage when sedentary.

How much the sedentary sluggishness can add up to is indicated by Dr. Lucien A. Brouha's comments at a conference at the University of California:

"Over 2000 healthy college students took part in the tests with the Harvard step test," he told the assembled industrial engineers. "This group included men of low physical efficiency (sedentary) as well as varsity athletes in excellent condition. It was found that the capacity to withstand the stress of hard muscular work was ten times as great in the fit as in the unfit (sedentary)."

> We have a right to feel tired on sedentary work because it lets the body slump to a less efficient level. . . . But we also have the right to push, pull, carry, stretch, stoop, lift, climb, grunt every day to keep the body in condition so that it is less vulnerable to tired feelings.

3. People with bosses are vulnerable

A century ago most people were farmers, independent

craftsmen, or proprietors of small businesses. They were mostly their own bosses.

Today, most people work for a boss. The smaller boss works under a slightly larger boss, and so on up the organization.

People are more likely to feel tired when working for someone else than when doing similar work for themselves. They are also likely to work harder when it is for themselves. This, no matter how perfect the boss may be. It's just in the cards that working for oneself is much different.

Sad to state, many bosses are far from perfect. Unless they mend their ways they (a) clash too often with workers' personalities, and (b) make the work situation too restrictive. This does not mean that the boss should be "easy," or that he should become palsy-walsy and use soft soap in the expectation that this would make him less of a cause of tired feelings.

We devoted an entire book, *The New Psychology of Leadership,* to a summary of research findings which show how the boss can become less clashing and less restrictive. The boss who bosses in ways that are least likely to make workers feel more tired than they should is described by workers in the following ways:

> "My boss often asks my opinion about how a job should be done."
> "He often gives me a chance to be on my own."
> "He talks over changes with me before they are decided upon."
> "He gives recognition for good work."
> "My boss looks out for the workers' interests."
> "He is helpful, not critical or fault-finding."

THE NEW STYLE

Business and social groups are getting an increasing share of new-style leaders. These trained leaders are displacing the old-style, who elbowed their way up

Old-style bosses (Autocratic)

Knew it all; made decisions himself, then pushed to make the decisions workable.

Talked aggressively. Tried to get people to follow him by talking or arguing them into it.

Felt that good pay for an honest day's work was enough for anyone.

Kept others in the dark about future plans or proposed changes. Did the planning himself. "I."

Tried to control others by having strict rules and giving orders. Discipline and penalties.

Kept his distance, so they would respect him and obey when he spoke.

Policy of finding fault on theory they would work harder, or not ask for a raise. Put on pressure.

Felt that the attitudes, ideals, goals he told them to have were what they would have.

Acted on theory that success of an undertaking depended on the judgment and hard work of a few gifted people (such as himself). "My goal."

IN LEADERSHIP

*"doing what came naturally" in handling
people. This comparative listing shows some
of the basic differences in the two styles.*

New-style leaders (Democratic)

Feels his way. Asks questions; gets help from those concerned as he
reaches decisions.

Brief in talking. Listens to learn what others think, or know, or feel,
and leads through their own ideas.

Adds a "mental wage" of congenial work groups and a feeling of being
appreciated.

Keeps members of social or group work up to date on what may be
in store; often works out plans with them. "We."

Not much dependence on rules and penalties; more freedom of discussion to bring out the best in others.

Acts as human as the next one. Closer to the group, and they follow
him for other reasons than his authority or wealth.

More use of encouragement and helping others solve their business
and social problems. Eases frustrations.

Realizes such thinking is picked up from work crews and other groups
they belong to, so leads through these rather than by "preach-
ing."

Methods based on belief an organization succeeds by teamwork, people
pulling together all up and down the line. "Our goal."

"He is reasonable in enforcing the rules, and does not
threaten us."

"It is easy to talk over job problems with him."

"He is good at grooming men for promotions."

"He gives me work I can do best."

"I can count on my boss to look out for me, even if he has to
stick his neck out to do it."

"He lets workers help each other out."

"My boss has a knack for knowing how I feel about things."

"It's O.K. with him if we kid and talk on the job."

"He is good at having the right people work together."

"He teaches us new job skills."

"My boss thinks about the same as I do about things."

"He's all business, but he considers our interests when as-
signing work."

"He seldom flies off the handle, and can take the gaff without
acting flustered."

"He is a 'warm' sort of person who seems to like everybody
in general."

We have a right to feel tired when we work for another person, most right when the boss is of the old style. . . . But we
also have the right to develop tolerance for the ways of the
boss who does make us tired; maybe we can't learn to love
him, but we can toughen our skin so he doesn't get under it
so easily.

4. Organization men are vulnerable

Most moderns work for an organization. Organization life
is much different from family life, or the life of the independent craftsman or farmer, or the self-employed professional person.

The organization is the most efficient method yet hit

upon for doing business. But, unfortunately, organizations have many built-in features that are restrictive or anxiety-arousing to practically all employees, from the yard laborer

"A wonderful feeling." When this sole survivor of a shipwreck found himself alone on a small island, he wondered how he could possibly survive until help came.

Out of sheer boredom he decided he would try to build a hut. To his surprise he soon got excited about his project. He worked from sunrise to sunset. He thought only of finishing the job.

We have exaggerated a bit. But we haven't exaggerated what it can mean to start a project and see it through.

The person who becomes absorbed in his work isn't bothered by minor irritations, doesn't count the days until he can get away from it all.

From the booklet "Satisfaction Guaranteed." Courtesy The Connecticut Mutual Life Insurance Co.

to president. These features range from competition for promotions to job simplification and standard procedures which give workers scant leeway to "be themselves," or "to grow." You may want to refresh yourself on some of these by looking again at the list of restrictive situations given in Chapter 5.

This is a case where we have the bear by the tail and dare not let go. The organization is unexcelled at producing goods and services economically. It will therefore not only be retained, but also will probably become more dominant in the future. This is not as hopeless as it may seem at first thought. A great deal can be done—and is being done by some organizations—to take out the bad and leave the good, either by revamping the setup or by a change of emphasis in its administration. These changes range from decentralization to retreading the bosses so they qualify as New-style Leaders.

A shorter work week, or more fringe benefits, or longer coffee breaks, or landscaped buildings, or better equipment, may all be appreciated by the workers. But such are frills and do not come near the core of the problem. The core, as shown by Dr. Frederick Herzberg's researches on "The Motivation to Work," is to make the individual's work more exciting, challenging, and satisfying *to him*. Work for an organization will not cause nearly as many tired feelings when it is set up and administered with that aim clearly and always in mind.

"The key to the future does not lie in the four-day week," Dr. Edwin G. Boring commented when presented with the Gold Medal of the American Psychological Foundation, "but in making work indistinguishable from play."

And Dr. Elliott Jaques told The Royal Society for the Promotion of Health that "working conditions which eliminate or prevent fatigue are the selfsame conditions which stimulate satisfaction and efficiency."

> There is less possibility of tired feelings when the worker can use his initiative, is given responsibility to carry a job through to completion, and gets from it a feeling of personal growth . . . a wonderful feeling that he is getting somewhere, and that heightens his will to work so that he doesn't think of feeling tired.

CHAPTER 16

Darwin's right to feel tired all the time

1. The peppy youth became a tired man

A million or more Americans are tired all the time, or are on the verge of being tired all the time, for much the same reasons that Charles Darwin was.

Darwin, one of the immortals of science, felt extremely tired all the time, probably hovering around step 7, 8, or 9 on the scale described in Chapter 13. Nevertheless, he worked, for at least forty years, regardless of that tiredness. Slowly he turned out 7000 pages of dazzling research which revitalized the study of natural science. Yet he could not revitalize himself, though he did learn how to live with and work in spite of his tired feelings.

140

A tall, powerfully built man, Darwin had the physique for heavy physical work. His ruddy complexion did not suggest that he was struggling against tiredness almost every minute. No one would have guessed by looking at him how tired he felt. But he had to carry an oak stick in the house, to lean on when he had a "weak spell." He would stop in the middle of a sentence while dictating, saying "I believe I mustn't do any more now."

During his growing years he had not been bothered by tiredness—rather the contrary. During his first twenty years he had enjoyed strenuous outdoor activities—mountain climbing, hunting, sports—with no complaint about feeling tired. He had spent his seventeenth summer exploring rugged Wales on foot, walking an average of thirty miles a day.

By the time he was twenty-five, however, it was becoming a different story. That year he confessed in his diary that he was plagued by tired feelings. The plague increased during the next half-dozen years, and then remained at a high level without ever letting up. The turning point at twenty-five might make us suspect something had happened that year which made him susceptible to tiredness from then onward. The most detailed study of his life indicates that the causes had started many years before that, and had been silently molding his inner self until, at twenty-five, the point of no return had been reached.

As we get acquainted with Darwin's life experiences these four points will be illuminated:

> Clashes and restrictions in early life may mold a person's inner self so that he becomes disposed to feel tired all the time, all the remainder of his life.
>
> The clashes and restrictions may belong to the past, but a dim memory of them can linger and cause a persistent

undercurrent of anxiety which upsets the balance in autonomics and endocrines.

Self-chosen work that is exciting, challenging and satisfying
makes it much easier to keep going despite the tired feelings that otherwise might be overwhelming.

Sympathetic help from a significant person enables the individual to get along better with his persisting tired feelings than would otherwise be possible.

2. Dr. Kempf's report on Darwin's tiredness

The most complete picture of the causes behind Darwin's
tiredness was first pieced together by Dr. Edward J. Kempf,
a present-day specialist in the tricks that mental tensions
play in human lives.

Physicians of Darwin's day could not understand what
kept him tired every minute. They begged the question by
calling it an "hereditary weakness," though none of his
eminent ancestors had shown it. That misleading phrase
"hereditary weakness" was especially unfortunate in his
case because it made him apprehensive that his children
would have it, too; this became a part of the anxieties that
perpetuated his tiredness.

It remained for Dr. Kempf, almost a century after Darwin's birth, to point out how anxiety dominated his private
world and made him feel tired. It was possible to unravel
the story with acceptable accuracy because of the vast
amount of recorded life detail about Darwin and his relatives.
We will follow Dr. Kempf's account, but in nontechnical
terms.

(Look back at Dr. Ffrench's findings near the close of
Chapter 2 to learn how prevalent anxiety tensions are today.)

Darwin was born with a sterling silver spoon in his mouth

and a wonderful brain in his head. His ancestors on both sides were of the gentry. On his father's side were successful physicians and outstanding scientists, on his mother's the businessmen of Wedgwood pottery fame. There was no "inherited weakness" from either side; presumably, a favorable start in life.

His father, who turns out to be the villain in the story, was two inches over six feet tall, weighed more than three hundred pounds. A successful physician who disliked the work which his father had forced him into, Charles's father dominated everyone. He was true, right, and wise, not to be questioned. Although adored by his women patients, those close to him were resentful of his bossiness and bored by his steady talking, especially his two-hour monologue before dinner. This was the man who, with the best of intentions, filled Charles's first twenty years with clashes and restrictiveness—friction and frustrations—so that the son's inner self became loaded with anxieties.

The impact of the father was all the greater in contrast with his gentle, understanding mother, whom the son idolized. She died when Charles was eight, leaving him with no safe harbor in which to seek refuge from his father's storms. She had given Charles sympathetic help and affection; from his father he received mostly criticism and threats to his self-esteem.

And, as with many parents who "know what is best," his father insisted upon the son's preparing for careers which the son did not want to follow. First, the father said Charles should become a physician, so he could take over the lucrative practice which the father himself hated. Charles was shipped off to medical school against his wishes. He disliked the medical courses, and failed them; he did well in a course in natural science which fascinated him.

The father was not the man to hide his disappointment that the son could not bail him out of his own disliked practice. "You will be a disgrace to yourself and all your family," he shouted at him in front of all the family.

Next his father decided that Charles should become a

From the booklet "Growing Pains." Courtesy The Connecticut Mutual Life Insurance Co.

A good way to start them on feeling tired the rest of their lives

small-town clergyman, and hustled him off to theology school. Worse than medical courses, the son felt; promptly he disgraced himself and all the family some more by failing those courses. He failed partly because he spent time drinking and gambling, and partly because he went on self-chosen natural history explorations when he might have been studying theology assignments.

When Darwin was twenty-two, his teacher of natural science urged him to join an expedition as naturalist on the ship *Beagle*, which was to survey uncharted coasts. His father objected, of course, and Charles wrote his sponsor that, "my father disliking, would take away all my energy."

That pathetic sentence sums up the crux of his tiredness —"my father disliking, would take away all my energy." And his father habitually disliked, disparaged, discouraged. Even when the scientific world began to accept Charles's research findings, his father still would not accept them.

This domineering and disparaging father was almost always in the back of Charles's mind, a ghost that threatened the son's self-esteem and kept him on edge with anxiety. When his father died, Charles was too tired to be able to go to the funeral.

3. How anxiety gives rise to tired feelings

Darwin's lasting tiredness was typical of that which occurs in people who live in a steady undercurrent of anxieties. The anxiety becomes disguised, so to speak, as a tired feeling. Experts believe that such anxiety accounts for the largest single share of chronic tiredness today. Perhaps it has always caused the lion's share; many children have been handled the way Darwin was—"papa knows best."

Dr. Raymond B. Cattell's factor analysis of personality and motivation show that the anxiety factor is highest during the teen years—the ages at which people are most likely to feel the clashes and restrictiveness of "papa knows best." After the teen years, Dr. Cattell finds that the anxiety usually tapers off. It does not taper off in some, like Darwin, whose inner selves have become molded into the habit of anxiety in the meantime.

There is an interesting difference between the anxiety of

most children and that of adults. In children the anxiety is usually about definite threats, such as of lightning or being punished. In adults it is more likely to center around some vague feeling, such as that one may not make good on a job, or that people may find fault with one.

Each of us has anxious moments now and then because of some definite threat. Dr. Hill's tests with the rowing crew, reported in Chapter 7, illustrated the role passing anxiety plays in upsetting the endocrine balance.

When the anxiety is not passing but lingers around, it may bring widespread changes in bodily functioning. Some of the changes due to continued anxiety have been reported by Drs. Cattell and Ivan Scheirer in their book *The Meaning and Measurement of Neuroticism and Anxiety*. They found that blood pressure and breathing rhythm are altered as anxiety is prolonged. There are many other bodily shifts which help upset the usual restorative processes of the body. The anxious person doesn't "just imagine" that he feels different inside; he *is* different inside.

These changes in bodily functioning are not necessarily permanent. They do last, however, as long as we remain anxious. As soon as we "forget" our anxiety, the functions shift back toward the normal balance and we achieve a steady state that no longer makes us feel worn out.

When we know clearly and definitely, as children usually do, what threatens us and causes our anxiety, it is easier to "forget" the anxiety. When we have to speak in public, for instance, and are apprehensive that we may fail, we get over our anxiety shortly after the situation changes and the threat in it has disappeared: we no longer feel tired over it.

Dr. Robert S. Schwab tells about the navigation officer on a combat ship who had an experience which shows the way passing anxieties can bring on severe tiredness. He had the light duty of working out convoy bearings. For three weeks this work had made him progressively tired, and he reported to the ship's doctor for help. Medicine and lighter duties did not relieve his tired feelings. It almost seemed that the navigator had a case of "combat fatigue." Then he received a letter bringing the news that his father did not have cancer, and that his wife's pregnancy did not have the previously suspected complications. Immediately upon receiving this good news his tired feelings left, and he was able to resume full duties. It was justified anxiety over home conditions that had made him feel tired.

But in people in a fix similar to Darwin's, some experiences earlier in life have molded an anxious attitude into them. They are anxious all or most of the time, without knowing exactly what they are anxious about.

Dr. Cattell's factor analysis of this state of mind leads him to describe it as a pervasive and prolonged dread of some nameless threat of being punished in some way. It does not arise from a current and real threat, but from past clashes and restrictions, such as his father imposed on Darwin.

The tired feelings of some mothers illustrate this vague dread, so that sometimes a mother of only one child is much more tired than another who has four children to "wear her down."

The difference is often due to the habit of anxiety which gives rise to vague dreads that something may threaten the child—germs, accidents, kidnapers, sex fiends, "hereditary weakness," or anything else the anxiety can be tied to. An habitually anxious mother of only one child can be much more tired out than the worry-free mother of a large brood. Children do make extra work, of course; it's not the work the children make, but the habit of worry that wears the mother down.

Experiments such as those by Dr. Daniel H. Funkenstein on "The Mastery of Stress" have shown that not everyone goes to pieces or becomes tired out when a real threat comes along. Approximately one person in four does worse than usual when in a threatening situation, but another one in four

From the booklet "Needlepoint." Courtesy The Connecticut Mutual Life Insurance Co.

Anxiety can make easy routine seem like a tiring rat race

rises to the challenge and does better than usual. Thus, anxiety over real threats weakens some people, while it puts starch in others.

Darwin was molded in youth so that he was weakened by anxiety. He came to be anxious when other people could see nothing to be anxious about—threatened by ghosts, or straw men. He would worry about possible disputes, for instance, and that self-made distress would disrupt the normal activity of autonomics and endocrines. His heart would race, he would feel sick to his stomach, go weak all over and have to lean on his oak stick.

The undercurrent of anxieties made sleep difficult. At forty-three he wrote, "my nights are always bad, and that stops my becoming vigorous." It is often that way with people who are

From the booklet "Needlepoint." Courtesy The Connecticut Mutual Life Insurance Co.

Would she have that pep if she were anxious?

quick to worry; they do not get the usual rest from their hours in bed, and start the next day feeling fagged out.

4. The "work cure" for tired feelings

Although hounded by his anxiety-born tiredness, Darwin had something else in his character which kept him doggedly at work, tired out or not. He was wealthy, and could have "enjoyed tiredness" and evaded work. But he had strong motivation to seek the truth from nature.

Idleness he detested. When only a young scientist he wrote a relative: "A man who dares to waste one hour of time has not discovered the value of life." He did not have the dependent make-up.

His motivation to be up-and-doing was strong enough to override some of his anxiety blockings, some of the time. In addition, he was lucky to have managed—over his father's objections—to work at something he found exciting, challenging, and satisfying. He systematically planned a schedule of activities, and followed it almost compulsively. The first hours of the day were set aside for his research. Several walks around his estate, rest periods, and business periods were duly scheduled and followed to the minute.

Anxious people have a special need for such a schedule. For one thing, it gives them a feeling of security, of being in familiar territory and safer from threats. Equally useful, a schedule cuts down the need to make spur-of-the-moment decisions about what to do next. Anxious people keep trapping themselves in quandaries of indecision. An "easy job" inspecting parts quickly tires out the anxious person because of the continuous decisions required.

Housework also illustrates the tiring nature of having to make decisions. Drs. Irma H. Gross and S. Howard Bartley observed the tiredness among some housewives who were doing their regular two-hour cleaning. Some of the women did not have a set routine for their cleaning, but had to make decisions as they went along. These women not only did a poorer job of cleaning, but they also were the first to tire out.

A set schedule, such as Darwin carefully followed, can cut down tiredness and inaction. His schedule probably gave him a grip on life and work which his tired feelings could have undermined without that assistance. Soon he was able to write that "work is my sole pleasure in life."

Sometimes his physician would feel that Darwin was over-doing, and would prescribe a week's rest at some watering resort. Darwin would obediently pack up—though the decisions to be made about what to pack wore him out—and go to the spa. Usually he returned before the week was up, not

He needs a "work cure." Ever since Joe won $100,000 on the Grand National Steeplechase he has wasted his days this way. You might not think so to see him now, but Joe used to be a star salesman.

Then he bought the winning ticket. He thought he was in clover. He quit his job and settled into a life of ease. After the novelty wore off he became irritable and restless. Though he couldn't admit it to himself, he missed the excitement of selling, the thrill all good salesmen get when a customer signs on the dotted line.

Joe's wife wishes he would stop hanging around the house, eternally slouched in front of the television set. Soon Joe will realize that he had the *real* winning ticket when he was top man on the company sales force.

From the booklet "Satisfaction Guaranteed." Courtesy The Connecticut Mutual Life Insurance Co.

because he felt any more rested but because he was impelled to get back to his work, his sole pleasure in life.

In cutting short his rest cures, Darwin may have shown better judgment than his physician. For one thing, life at the resort seemed more threatening to him, because while there he had to abandon the security of his customary routine. He was often seasick from anxiety on these "rests."

In addition, his work reduced his anxieties as only one other thing did. It usually does with those people who believe that man was put on this earth to use his abilities as best he can.

Work helps also because it keeps the person occupied so that he does not have as much free time to fret about threats. Systematic work, by schedule, can be occupational therapy which keeps anxious tired folk from going to pieces, and enables them to live more at peace with themselves. Often it is the best way to master one's tired feelings.

5. *The value of moral support from his wife*

His work . . . and his wife . . . were Darwin's salvation.

Emma Wedgwood, his cousin and wife, encouraged him, appreciated him, and thought him a great credit to the family —as his mother had, not threatening, the way his father had been. Darwin came to depend upon his wife's sympathetic help to support his spirits so he could keep going. Day and night he needed her presence. When he took his scheduled daytime naps, she sat patiently and quietly beside the couch. If anxiety made sleep difficult, he asked her to hold his hand for the reassurance it gave him. She was continually on watch to shield him from the threats of arguments, annoyances, and bores, and to give him reassurance.

She was unquestionably helpful in saving him from possible ruin. Modern mental specialists call this *supportive therapy,* and they make much use of it; often they insist that relatives and employers mend their ways so they can give the distraught person the encouragement and reassurance he may need desperately.

The world should be thankful that Darwin married the sort of woman he did. (His father, of course, had objected to the match.) Had his wife been a nagger, or a pusher, his story would have had a much different ending. But Emma Wedgwood was happy to play her role of mothering him in the way he needed, and thus prevented his bruised inner self from completely incapacitating him.

The right work and the right wife . . . or the right work and the right boss . . . make tired feelings much less of a problem than they would be otherwise, whatever the source of the tired feelings.

CHAPTER 17

Lincoln's right to feel tired one-fourth of the time

1. TIRED DESPITE GREAT PHYSICAL STRENGTH
2. THE "SAD LINCOLN" WAS A "TIRED LINCOLN"
3. TIREDNESS FROM DEPRESSED MOODS
4. TIRED FROM BALKED AMBITIONS OR SHATTERED HOPES
5. LINCOLN'S WORK CURE

1. Tired despite great physical strength

Another million or more Americans have Abraham Lincoln's variety of tired feelings, tiredness that comes and goes without physical work or bodily ailments to cause it. This tiredness, Lincoln's variety, is not due to anxiety but to depressed moods when discouragement threatens one's private world. The tired feelings come as the mood slows down, slowly vanish as the mood perks up. The person—those million or more—may feel tired for a day, but it is usually for a week or a month; then the feeling of tiredness lifts and he enjoys a feeling of pep for a while.

Lincoln's tiredness was complicated, however, by a rather

154

rare condition of his endocrines which we should describe at the outset of his story. When he was eleven he started to shoot upward in growth, and to complain about feeling tired. Within a few years he was four inches above six feet. This height came mostly in his legs and arms. Some of the bones of his face grew, too, especially the jaw and cheek bones. His hat size remained 7⅛. His trunk did not grow much. When he sat in a chair he was no taller than other young men. "He appears to be all joints," neighbors commented. These unusual proportions gave him a distinctive, attention-getting appearance the rest of his life.

Such excessive growth of some bones is usually due to a trick the pituitary gland plays. This pea-sized gland, nestled in the base of the skull, is the master gland of the endocrines. When it plays this trick the person is likely to have the physical strength of a giant, yet he will tire easily because the tricky pituitary has upset the balance in the endocrine glands.

So Lincoln had the muscle and bone for strenuous work, and occasionally did hard work in his youth. He was tough and wiry, they said, and as strong as three ordinary men. Wrestling was the popular way to prove one's strength on the frontier, and he was the champion in his locality. People who knew Abe told Carl Sandburg that Abe's hands were so strong he could grasp the far end of an ax handle with only one hand and hold the ax out at arm's length in a straight line with his arm.

Lincoln preferred, however, not to do hard work. John Romaine, who hired him for manual labor, commented, "He said to me one time that his father taught him to work, but never taught him to love it." Romaine also said Lincoln "was awfully lazy." That is often said of those who are struggling mightily against feelings of tiredness.

Much of the time Lincoln felt too tired to move energetically. This showed in his slow and quiet speech. When he sat, he slumped. When he stood up he slumped as tired people are likely to do. One time another unusually tall man wanted to compare his height with Lincoln's, and they stood back to back. They were of equal height it seemed, until Lincoln pulled his bones together and stood up to his full height.

"You see," Lincoln said, "there's a lot of 'come-out' in me." Usually he felt too tired to "come-out."

His favorite working position was probably due to this tiredness. At the office he sat tilted back in a chair, shoes off, feet on the table. His law partner said Lincoln sometimes sat that way most of the day, looking at the ceiling and thinking. At home, he stretched his long legs across the floor, shoes and coat off, back reclining against a kitchen chair he had up-ended so the slats would provide a sloping backrest. An undignified, improper position, his fastidious wife called it. But it remained his favorite.

2. The "Sad Lincoln" was a "Tired Lincoln"

By the time Lincoln reached his twenties another cause was looming up to add to the tiredness his pituitary may have started. This was first emphasized by Dr. L. Pierce Clark, a Lincoln admirer, in a thorough study of the spells of depressed moods which came over Lincoln. These moods were probably the more serious factor in Lincoln's adult tiredness, as is the case with a million or more adults today. (Two of Dr. Ffrench's tired people were depressed.)

Anyone who has had a minor spell of the blues has had a taste of how depressed spirits can slow one down and bring on tiredness and inactivity. Sometimes the downcast person infers that it is the tiredness that causes the blues. But it is the other way around; one of the first symptoms of the blues is to feel tired.

As Lincoln grew into manhood, he developed king-size spells of the blues. The first serious spell was following the death of his fiancée, Ann Rutledge. He was stunned by the blow and plunged into a profound depression. For weeks following her death he sat silently, or wandered aimlessly, seemingly oblivious of his surroundings. The neighbors understood, and gave him help and encouragement. It was more than grief: grief plus a deeply depressed mood.

Never much of a talker unless he had to talk, during his depressed periods he would be silent as a sphinx for days. There were apathetic weeks when his slowed spirits disrupted his control of his actions so thoroughly that he could scarcely bring himself to move.

By the time he was thirty, these bouts with depressed spirits had left their marks on his face. His underlip drooped during his melancholy moods, and the droop became permanent. The sad-faced expression made him look older than his years, and friends began to call him "Old Abe." "He often shed dry tears," they said of him. He became practically two men in one. There were cheerful weeks between spells of depression. Then he felt life was worth living and joking about; his actions were not blocked then by tiredness. This was the Laughing Lincoln, who laughed, probably, to keep the doleful thoughts under cover.

But there was also the Sad Lincoln every now and then, increasingly so. When sad he felt as though his luck had run out, and life had only dark sides for him. The slowed mood would disorganize his inner self and tired feelings paralyzed him so that he became scarcely a spectator of life.

3. Tiredness from depressed moods

Specialists think that a large share of tiredness today is due to the same factor that was the bane of Lincoln's adult years

—periods of depressed spirits. The moods do not have to be as severe as Lincoln's to overwhelm the person with tired feelings.

These spells come without any obvious reason, though there is a reason. We recall from Chapter 12 that the feeling of despair is the big brother of tired feelings. A depressed period is a period of despair.

In between tired spells in these instances there is often a zestful period, free of despair, in which the person feels brimming with energy and works tirelessly without having to push himself to do so. This is commonly shown by some high-pressure executives and star salesmen who have their "good weeks" and "bad weeks."

This tiredness that goes with depressed moods is reported to be slightly more prevalent among women than men. It is more likely to occur among the well educated, the ambitious, and the likable sort. Between the ages of forty and fifty it inclines to flare up and become worse in both sexes.

The person may feel only mildly dejected—mild, but it is sufficient to take the starch out of him. The tiredness continues as long as the mood continues.

The first intimation that low spirits are just around the corner is almost always just plain tiredness that cannot be accounted for. Initiative is lowered. One's actions are slowed down, and some may be skipped because the person is "too tired to do it."

What brings on these periods?

4. Tired from balked ambitions or shattered hopes

A clue to what brings this condition on is found in the fact that it occurs mostly in well-educated and ambitious people. It appears to be precipitated by some threat to their aspirations. Those who have easy aspirations, or who are satisfied with things as they are, should be relatively free from this variety of tiredness.

It is the eager beaver who is more likely to have it. He is eager to get ahead, or to achieve something, something he has chosen for himself. But he is balked in achieving it and he

Contented . . . no tired feelings. Bossy is the placid type. Nothing excites her. Nothing moves her. She isn't going anywhere. She just wants to stand in one spot, munching grass.

There are people who think Bossy leads the perfect life. No work to do, no responsibilities, nothing to worry about. No joys. No sorrows. Life in a vacuum.

For those who are satisfied to stand still, Bossy's life is ideal.

> From the booklet "Satisfaction Guaranteed." Courtesy The Connecticut Mutual Life Insurance Co.

begins to feel there is nothing he can do about it, as Lincoln felt when Ann Rutledge died. Then comes the hopelessness and tiredness. There are three ways people react to this dilemma.

A few people give up and remain on the gloomy, tired-out side of life. This is the way taken by some people who "go into a decline" when they reach retirement age.

Some manage during their brooding to adjust their ambitions and private worlds so they can resume life with some of their old zest. This was probably what Lincoln did; he kept holding on until he could see things in a more encouraging light.

Some others convince themselves that they could reach their aims by excessive application, and they swing into overly optimistic moods and become "balls of fire" at getting things done. Supersalesmen and promoters who make and lose fortunes are often of this sort.

Lincoln had many balked ambitions and shattered hopes, although his father did not raise him to be ambitious. In fact, his father did little about raising him except to knock him off the rail fence one day when Abe made a smart-aleck comment to a neighbor. His father was a slow, careless, uneducated man who did carpentering. He didn't hunt jobs but waited for them to come to him; a contented-cow sort of person. Yet in a sense Lincoln got his ambitions from his shiftless father—the son in his teen years determined not to be like him.

It is the goals and ambitions which one sets for oneself which are most cherished and which cause most turmoil in the private world when something restricts one from reaching the goal. Lincoln was his own goal-setter; his goals were not handed him by teachers, parents, or bosses, and consequently he was intensely motivated by his goals and hopes.

It was Abe's own idea to educate himself. Altogether he had only four months of formal schooling, which was about par for the time and place. His shrewd but ignorant father hated books, perhaps because he couldn't read them. When

Abe was twenty—the same year and age that Darwin was flunking out of medical school—his father complained to a visitor that "Abe has got the fool idea of eddication in his head, and it can't be got out."

Lincoln set his ambitions on many other goals which fizzled, one after the other, through no fault of his. Many of these fizzles plunged him into deep funks and tired spells during which he inwardly adjusted his aims so he could emerge and start again. He was a many-time loser, yet each time he recovered control of his frustrated mood to rise and fight again—this in spite of the expectation of failure which came to haunt him. At the time of his immortal Gettysburg Address, for example, he was tired and wanted to be left alone; he expected his brief remarks to be a total failure.

A person who has only modest ambitions and reasonable hopes can run into frustrations, too. We are all being restricted in one way or another, all the time. Perhaps more so now than a century ago, as Chapter 15 and other sections of this book have suggested.

This widespread cause for tired feelings might be cut down if, as Sir Heneage Ogilvie told physicians in a symposium on stress: ". . . we could hypnotise men into marrying girls they disliked, replace successful executives in order to reinstate worthy but second-rate colleagues, grant all-around increases in salary, and give every man a bigger house, a smarter car and a prettier and better-tempered wife than his neighbor."

And to Canadian physicians Dr. W. B. Spaulding said: "It is probable that much of the everyday fatigue of normal people represents one aspect of a mild, passing state of depression related to such things as boredom, frustrations at work or at home, a feeling that one's efforts are unappreciated, and so on. . . . In our fast-moving civilization where material success and a driving ambitious attitude toward life tend to be over-emphasized, people may occasionally glimpse the relative futility of their exertions and suffer a let-down, tired feeling."

5. Lincoln's work cure

Having no inherited wealth, Lincoln had to work to eat. Fortunately, as with Darwin, he had some character qualities which made him regard work as the right thing. This helped him come back after frustrations which would have taken the heart out of lesser men. And he slowly learned how to live with his tired feelings—master them—by plugging along, regardless of them.

So he worked, though he usually did not feel like it. Plunging into work did not increase his tiredness. On the contrary, the work diverted his thoughts and he almost forgot the sadness and tiredness as long as he worked. He said he kept a grip on himself by big doses of work.

His biggest hurdle was starting work when he felt downcast and tired. This was complicated by two factors: he had not given attention to being systematic, and his occupation did not demand a set timetable for doing things.

His "filing system" is an example. He stuck legal papers, notes for speeches, letters to answer, into a drawer, or pocket, or into his 7⅛ hat—all on a hit or miss basis. The nearest he came to a filing system was one envelope in his desk on which he had written: "When you can't find it anywhere else, look in this."

"He was regularly irregular," commented his close friend Joshua Speed, "with no stated time for eating, no fixed time for going to bed, none for getting up."

If Lincoln could have scheduled his work and routines, as Darwin did, it would have been easier for him to pull himself together and push ahead when seized by tiredness. But as it

was, when he most needed to get into action he was in no
frame of mind to decide what to do.

When the tall man compared his height with Lincoln's, the

WE FINISHED IT IN ONE FELL SWOOP
OF 15 HOURS. WHEW ! **WHAT
A WONDERFUL DAY** !

RAMA

The work cure. You're looking at a happy man. Tired, but not depressed. Who wouldn't be tired after the day he put in? But he'll
bounce back quickly, stimulated by that glorious feeling of having
reached a goal.

Ed and his crew had a deadline to meet. They started early and
kept right at it until they were satisfied with their work.

Who cares about hours at times like these? There is nothing like
the fun of working with people for the sheer joy of accomplishing a
worthwhile purpose. This is when life surges with excitement.

A wonderful day indeed!

From the booklet "Satisfaction Guaranteed." Courtesy
The Connecticut Mutual Life Insurance Co.

challenger was awed by Abe's "come-out." Lincoln showed
his "come-out" again and again by achieving regardless of
his engulfing tiredness. This "come-out" would have been

easier, and more certain, had he set up a schedule to guide him when he needed guidance most.

Tired feelings are here to stay. We can expect to have them at times, perhaps all the time if we are of the anxious sort. But we can usually use our "come-out" and work regardless of them.

As a closing thought we quote from Dr. Roger G. Bannister about the "come-out" some people have for really exhausting activity, such as running long distances. (He was the first man to run a mile in less than 4 minutes, and was a member of the team that set the world's record for the 4-mile relay. As a physician, he was naturally interested in muscular effort.) In a special issue of the *British Medical Bulletin* which was devoted to work and effort he wrote:

> Yet the difference between athletes lies not entirely in differences in cardiac output and diffusion capacity; it lies rather, I suspect, in their capacity for mental excitement, which brings with it an ability to overcome or ignore the discomfort—even pain—in muscles and the brain which is probably caused by ischaemia and the consequent changes of blood lactate concentration and *p*H. . . . Psychological and other factors beyond the ken of physiology set the razor's edge of defeat or victory and determine how closely an athlete approaches the absolute limits of performance.

CHAPTER 18

What the individual can do to master his tired feelings

How can a person apply all this varied information in his own life and work? This chapter will summarize a couple of dozen important points that should guide the individual in mastering his tired feelings. To give "something he can take hold of," we will spell out this summary in rather dogmatic statements which can serve as guides, or rules.

The first six summaries are general in nature. The others get down to brass-tack details.

1. It takes time to master tired feelings. It may take only a week, if you're lucky. It is more likely to take six months.

2. It requires a great deal of self-direction, especially when hostile attitudes or self-pity are factors in the tired feelings—and they are often strong factors. You are likely to have to be firm with yourself on some points.

3. Very often it requires cooperation from your employer who could make your work less tiring by proper attention to your equipment, environment, and supervision.

4. Don't expect you can do something so that you will never feel tired again. Tiredness is part of living. There will be hot days, and harder-than-usual work, and passing annoyances to make you feel tired. We have to learn to put up with a touch of tired feelings from time to time, and work in spite of not feeling like it.

5. When tired feelings linger around most of the time, or are so strong they interfere with work or comfort, they should be looked upon as a warning that something out of the ordinary needs to be corrected.

A searching medical examination is essential when the feelings are lingering or intense. It will take at least a half hour, and possibly three or four days, before the laboratory tests can be completed. Your firm may be staffed to do this, a few are; otherwise go to your family physician. If he cannot find a reason for the tired feelings, ask him to refer you to a clinic or internist who has more equipment for tracking down hidden ailments.

If nothing amiss is found in your body that needs correction, then it will be your attitudes, working and living habits, or environmental situations that need to be corrected. Often some of each of these are involved. The remainder of these guides deal primarily with these aspects.

6. What if the medical tests reveal *no* body ailment to cause the tired feelings, which is the case in about three out of four people who have persistent and severe tiredness? Then the best thing to do is to work as if you did not have tired feelings. It may be difficult to believe until you try it a few days, but you will not feel as tired when you are diligently working and keeping your mind on your work.

The remaining summaries, or guide rules, apply more to some people than to others. After you decide that one applies to you, use self-direction to correct the situation whenever it is under your control. If it isn't under your control, then use self-direction to put up with it or to get away from it.

7. *Overweight* people tire easily. If you are more than ten pounds overweight, you had better control your eating habits and get back down to size.

8. *Sedentary* people tire easily. If you have white-collar work, or light factory work (handling parts that weigh less than ten pounds), you are probably sedentary unless you get some strenuous off-the-job workouts, regularly, not just once in a while.

Each day you should get at least a half hour of brisk walking (almost a trot), or five minutes of brisk stair climbing (if you are under sixty, don't use the hand rail, and do take some of the steps two at a time), or five minutes of lifting or tugging at your maximum strength.

If you haven't been getting that much activity, regularly each day, start now with an easy amount that will not wear you down. Then gradually increase the length and forcefulness of the activity from day to day so that your steady state becomes limbered up. If you can get yourself into condition so you can do more than the minimum described in the preceding paragraph, so much the better for you.

Conventional setting-up exercises are not strenuous enough to take much sedentariness out of a person. Massage and vibration also do not fill the bill; you have to work your muscles yourself, and hard enough to produce some beneficial results on their strength and staying power.

9. People who have *short or poor sleep* tire out easily the next day. Some can get along on six hours a night, others need ten. Physiologists believe that around seven hours of good sleep provides all the rest the average person needs.

Short sleep, or poor sleep does not deplete the energy supply significantly. But it does make it more difficult to keep your mind on your work the next day, and you are much more irritable than usual. Thus you are more susceptible to clashes and restrictive situations. The day's clashes and restricted feelings are likely to be taken to bed and make the night's sleep poor, as the chartoon pictures. Break this vicious

"THIS GUY'S A CINCH TO BLOW HIS LID: ALL DAY IT'S BUSINESS BUSINESS; ALL NIGHT IT'S BUSINESS BUSINESS ALL OVER AGAIN."

Recognize yourself? If you do, it's time to reorganize yourself.

Don't let unsolved problems of the day pursue you all night. As problems arise during the day, solve them. Make your decisions, then forget about them. Most problems can be divided into two groups: those you can do something about and those over which you have no control.

And if you find yourself lying awake, don't fret about lack of sleep. We do need rest. So if you can't sleep, take it easy. You'll feel much better in the morning.

From the booklet "The Worry-Go-Round." Courtesy The Connecticut Mutual Life Insurance Co.

cycle by solving some of your clashes and restrictiveness as will be suggested in later guides. (More about this in our book *Sound Ways to Sound Sleep*, which is a companion to the book you are reading now.)

10. People who *sit slumped* over desks or work benches are likely to get tired backs. Dr. Hans Kraus, physiatrist at Bellevue Medical Center, found that four out of five cases of low-back tiredness were due to back muscles that had been weakened. The weakening came either from not being used enough to keep them strong, or from poor posture.

Use a posture chair. Keep it properly adjusted for your particular build and work. Executive-type posture chairs usually flatter the man's ego more than they help his back. The executive would be better off if he used the same chair he provides for the clerks.

In case you do not have a posture chair, then work sitting on an ordinary chair with a firm seat. Sit on your sitting bones (not thighs) on the front half of the seat. Don't lean against the back. Sit tall, both feet on the floor—balanced, but not rigid.

Years of slumped sitting may have brought you into such a condition that you also need special exercises to strengthen your back muscles. An orthopedist, physical therapist, physiatrist, or many gymnasium instructors can show you suitable exercises.

By the way—how is your sitting posture right this moment? This is a good time to take the slump out and sit balanced and tall, on the front of a firm seat.

11. People who *stand* most of the day are likely to get tired legs and feet. The wrong shoes (in women, especially), poor standing posture, and not enough movement cause this trouble.

Standing is usually more tiring than walking because the

muscles are not moved enough to "pump" blood back to the heart. If you have a standing job, "pump" the muscles by moving around more, and by contracting the calves several times an hour. Also see if you can plan the work so that you can sit at the job from time to time.

Watch your standing posture. Stand tall and balanced, but not rigid. Weight should be on the balls of your feet. Put a little more weight on one foot for a while, then shift it to the other, then on both. No sway back, no hip switch, or belly sag. Chin up.

12. People who keep *muscles too tense* tire out easily, partly because of the work it takes to keep muscles contracted, partly because the tenseness may make muscles actually sore. And especially because anxious people are inclined to keep muscles too tense (anxiety tension which Dr. Ffrench—Chapter 2—found in 26 of 105 tired people he examined). This was also illustrated by the typists who felt tired in their necks rather than in their working fingers.

Unwind yourself. Do two things to start unwinding. (1) Make it a practice to tense no more than is necessary to do the task, and only in the muscles being used for that task— easy does it. (2) Form the habit of *relaxed working*—intentionally relax the muscles not used in the work.

To relax them, simply do the opposite of what you do when you brace yourself. Brace a muscle momentarily, then do the opposite and keep it relaxed. Work "loosy"—loose and easy. More about the techniques of loosy working in our book *Practical Business Psychology.*

Impertinent, perhaps, but are you braced or relaxed at this moment? What earthly reason is there for you to have tensed muscles now! Better do just the opposite and relax a few of them, deliberately. Pause to relax muscles and you'll really refresh yourself, especially if you keep relaxed after the pause.

13. *Bored* people tire easily. If your work is not interesting to you, develop some skills that will qualify you for more interesting work.

From the booklet "The Next Promotion." Courtesy The Connecticut Mutual Life Insurance Co.

Boredom on retirement because they have time on their hands and nothing to do. Age forty is none too early to begin developing outside interests and activities that will keep us both interested and active upon retirement.

Perhaps you can make your present work less boresome by changing your pace from time to time. Or add some "game interest" by keeping a record of your output each hour. Or simply change from sitting to standing, and back again, to break the monotony. Sometimes these help.

The coffee break is useful chiefly to break the monotony. The same for music while you work. Some workers use daydreams to lessen the boredom.

A sure way is to get the boss either to assign you to work that is more interesting, or to give you more variety (less job simplication) to make the present work more challenging and interesting.

Workers during slack seasons, and retired people, often become bored and feel tired because they do not have enough to do to keep them occupied.

14. *Ambitious* people tire easily, not necessarily because they work harder, but primarily because they often become anxious about not being as successful as they had wished—anxiety tensions, again. It usually takes a lot of self-control for the eager beaver to settle upon more reasonable ambitions, and to be satisfied with an older model automobile. He also needs practice in relaxed working.

15. People who *feel they are not going to be able to better their lot* tire easily. This is related to the preceding guide, and to old-fashioned inferiority complexes. Discouragement may be followed by the despair reaction and tired feelings. This is as difficult to control as too much ambition, and is probably more widespread among the rank and file. Both may require some assistance by a counselor.

Sometimes the boss can help as counselor. He can also help by delegating some details and in general helping the individual develop himself. He can get some pointers on doing this from our book *The Techniques of Delegating*.

16. People who *feel left out of the crowd* tire easily—The Lonely Crowd. This applies to most people, but becomes acute with the worker who is not "accepted" by the others in his crew. This also becomes a potent cause of tired feelings

with the person who wants keenly to be popular and in the swim.

As with ambitions, it takes a lot of self-direction to adjust

RAMA.

Having a wonderful time. For this man retirement from a successful career represented an exciting new phase of his life.

Now he sees only the people he and his wife really like. He worries no more about building up good contacts. He enjoys the freedom to be himself.

From the booklet "The Next Promotion." Courtesy
The Connecticut Mutual Life Insurance Co.

this desire so one does not become worn out by anxiety about it.

Size up your workmates. Figure how they want members of the team to dress, act, talk, think, and work. Adapt yourself to fit better into the group. Or ask for a transfer to a group that you fit better. This applies to neighbors, also.

17. People tire out easily when they *have to be with people they dislike*. You can't always avoid people you dislike, but sometimes you can talk it over with the boss and be transferred. Sometimes you can get to know the person better—or even talk over with him about how he irritates you—and discover that he is no longer such a pain in the neck. Sputtering about the person is no help. Talking it over can be a great help.

This is sometimes not solved, as the chartoon shows, until retirement. Until that time, you might as well put up with such individuals.

18. People who have *personal problems*—love, money, work, relatives, neighbors, homeliness, what not—tire out easily. This is another situation in which talking it over is useful, especially if the problem is talked over with a more experienced person who can lead you to some workable solution.

19. People tire easier when they *have to make decisions*. This is one reason why personal problems and jobs which require many decisions are tiring. And, to make matters worse, decisions become more tiring when a person already feels tired—another vicious cycle.

Two helps: set up a schedule that will make as many things as possible routine (as Darwin did), and also set up some general policies (such as "never argue with a customer") that will almost automatically make the unavoidable decisions for you.

And relax yourself, not only when you have to make decisions, but also right now, because we suspect you have wound yourself up again since reading guide No. 12.

20. People tire out easily when they have to *do work they did not help plan*. This may seem to be opposed to the guide just given; the critical part this time is not making the de-

cisions but in having a measure of self-determination. This is actually a variant of the following guide, but merits separate mention because it is a widespread cause of tired feelings among workers.

21. People tire out when they are *bossed,* or have to do things they are not interested in doing, or do not want to do. There is a lot of this in our world. About all we can do to master tired feelings from this source is to grin and bear it, or become hermits.

People tend to brace themselves when bossed. Try deliberate relaxing the next time you are given an order, or assigned a task you do not want to do.

The boss himself can do much to cut down this cause of tired feelings. There are many pointers for him in our book *The New Psychology for Leadership.*

22. People tire out easily when they are *criticized,* reprimanded, laughed at, or belittled. It is hard to learn to take these. Relaxing helps.

There are fewer tired feelings if we talk the fault-finding over, and promptly. Sometimes we can talk it over with the critic himself; if not with him, then with someone who can give sympathetic help and guidance.

And be man enough to admit that sometimes the critic is right, and act accordingly.

23. People tire out when they do *strenuous physical work,* but this is the "good kind" of tiredness and seldom causes troublesome tired feelings. In sedentary persons it may cause stiff muscles as well as tiredness.

When this kind of work is done, about fifteen to twenty minutes every hour should be spent resting—more rest when the person is over fifty years old, or is not used to such heavy work. The older or sedentary person should rest as soon as his pulse reaches one hundred and ten a minute.

Relaxing should be a bit different during rest pauses in strenuous work. There will be less muscle soreness the next day if the muscles used in the work are moved under their own power during the rest—but gently! This is similar to the "pumping" that helps when standing for long periods.

Work was continuous movement of three controls so as to bring four steadily shifting pointers back to zero.

Data from Drs. G. F. Hauty and R. B. Payne

Better motivation, less slump, when they were promised a rest break before starting work

For lighter jobs, such as conveyor assembly of light parts, five minutes rest an hour is generally recommended.

It is interesting that a person is given a lift by merely knowing that he will have a rest pause in due course. This is illustrated by the chartoon.

The only time "quick-energy foods," such as candy bars or sweetened drinks, are useful in cutting down tired feelings is when hard exercise is continued for several hours, such as a twenty-mile walk or marathon race. Best results are obtained when the candy is nibbled during the course of the work, say a bite every half hour.

24. As people *grow older,* they tire out sooner, especially when doing physical work or rapid work. Men who are in good physical condition, and not sedentary, begin to slow down in recuperating from hard exercise at around age 50, and to lose in muscular endurance at around age 55. Rapid movements begin to tire them more at around age 40.

Be your age in pace and load. As Elihu Root said on his ninetieth birthday, "I can work just as hard as ever I worked —for one hour a day."

25. When people are in *hot or humid* locations they tire out sooner, whether they are working or not. When the surrounding temperature goes above 78°F, the steady state is knocked out of balance in its efforts to get rid of the body heat.

Turn on the air conditioner, or take longer rest pauses. If you are perspiring much, take salt tablets with lots of water.

26. People tire out easily when they are in *noisy locations.* It is not known whether the noise affects the body directly or not, although intense noise can produce deafness in the course of time.

In offices, homes, and most assembly jobs the tiring effect is probably due largely to noise interfering with hearing and talking—it is restrictive. To some people it is also annoying. As a rule of thumb, if you have to raise your voice to carry on a conversation, the location is too noisy to be good.

Noisy machines should be quieted, or isolated.

Offices and homes can be made quieter by carpets and acoustical ceilings that absorb noise. Many machines, such as punch presses, make too much noise to be reduced by acoustical ceilings. You can find details about making a home or office quieter in our book *Increasing Personal Efficiency*.

But what can you do about street and traffic noises! They are something else we apparently just have to put up with.

27. People tire out easily when they have to do eye work in *poor light*. This does not occur often in business, but does happen. It is frequent in homes, where the lighting is likely to be planned to "look pretty" rather than to provide for efficient seeing. More details about this in the book just mentioned.

28. People tire out easily when, for whatever reason, they *feel sorry for themselves*. Feel that way if you must, but you will be better off in many ways if you just keep on working —and in a loosy fashion.

> The man is fortunate whose work tires him, gives him a good appetite, and promotes a good night's sleep.
> —Dr. David B. Dill, Scientific Director,
> Medical Section, U.S. Army Chemical Center

CHAPTER **19**

What the employer should do

Memorandum for the President
SUBJECT: Employees' tired feelings and
   a plan for company-wide action.

I

The company has a stake in T.F. (tired feelings) because
T.F. interfere with the will to work. At any time during a
work shift at least one out of four workers feels tired and
wants to stop what he is doing; some do stop, others half stop.
T.F. are also regarded as a factor in

absenteeism	grievances
accidents	labor turnover
alcoholism	restricted output
errors and quality	

II

T.F. are seldom due to excessive muscular exertion on the
job, or to the depletion of the person's energy supply. (See

table "The Energy People Have for Work," in Chapter 6.)
T.F. are more prevalent among office workers than laborers.

More use of machine power can lower T.F. on some
strenuous jobs, but the mechanization of lighter jobs often
increases T.F. because

> Workers then become too sedentary
> Operations become simplified so that workers are bored

Actions to take:

(a) Measure physiological stress of heavier jobs to find
where "muscle-saving" is needed.
(b) Take steps to counteract sedentariness on light jobs,
and boredom on simplified routine jobs.

III

Some workers' T.F. are not directly due to their work, but the
company has as much stake in them as if the decreased will
to work were caused by the job.

1. About one out of ten workers has T.F. because of some
unsuspected physical ailment which can usually be corrected.

Actions to take:

(a) Prompt medical examinations of those who complain
about persisting T.F.
(b) Annual examinations of hourly-rated employees as well
as of executives, as a preventative measure.

2. About one out of five has T.F. because of poor health
habits

alcoholism	poor sleep
overweight	sedentariness
poor posture	unbalanced diet

Actions to take:

    (a) A continuing company-wide educational program.

    (b) Individual advice at time of annual medical examination and follow-up.

3. One out of four adults (actual survey figure) report having had gnawing personal problems and these can undermine their will to work and produce T.F.

Actions to take:

    (a) Suitable counseling to help solve the immediate problem.

    (b) Suitable counseling to relieve their anxiety tensions and teach them methods of relaxing as a preventative measure.

IV

Environmental influences on the job have a part in causing T.F., but the importance of these is not known in all instances. A comfortable work place, however, is desirable for securing employees in a tight labor market.

decoration	noise and vibration
housekeeping	odors, ventilation
lighting	temperature, humidity
music	

Actions to take:

    (a) Find out what the going standards are in the locality, and take steps to equal or exceed them.

    (b) Find out what environmental factors employees complain about, and act accordingly.

V

Work arrangement and methods have been proven important in producing T.F. at times.

difficult-to-read dials, etc.
pace, repetitive or unvarying
posture arrangements, poor or missing
rest pauses, inadequate or poorly spaced
sequence does not give goal-gradients

Actions to take:

(a) Physiological stress measurements to guide in arranging rest pauses.
(b) Medical advice on posture arrangements.
(c) Consulting industrial psychologist for advice on other aspects.

VI

Human factors on the job—relations with others, and the individual's deep desires—are now believed to account for the bulk of T.F. The engineer or financier who is used to dealing with tangible things often finds these human factors difficult to grasp; this may explain why practical men have overlooked them as causes of T.F.

Relation with others	*Deep desires*
competition with other workers	how-do-I-stand-with-the-boss anxiety
conversation restricted, difficult	
feel discriminated against	lay-off anxiety
job does not seem important	promotion anxiety
praise, recognition not received	quality anxiety
supervision not satisfying	responsibility, authority not given
teammates not congenial	rules, procedures restrictive
	sub-goals absent
	work planned by others, not self
	work not personally satisfying

Actions to take:

(a) Review company policies and procedures in view of above factors, and consider modifications.

(b) Special counseling to help individual workers adjust to unsatisfying or irritating factors.

(c) Special training for leadmen, supervisors, and executives to enable them to understand these human factors and be guided more by them in their dealings with their workers.

VII

Our survey has shown that T.F. in the firm cannot be solved by some gadgets or more mechanization, as we had hoped. A continuing attack on a rather wide front is needed. Specialized technical information is required for the men who are responsible for reducing T.F. among the employees.

For a company with 300 employees a fully adequate program would require:

1 full-time physician trained in industrial medicine and with special training in muscle physiology

1 full-time clinical psychologist (Ph.D.) with special training in industrial sociology

Reporting directly to the President or General Manager

1 part-time consulting industrial psychologist to work with Personnel on selection and placement, and with Methods on job procedures.

The job functions of the full-time men would be as follows; the most important long-range function is given first:

Industrial Physician	*Clinical Psychologist*
1. Health education, plant-wide	1. Human factors education for
dietary balance	leadmen up
muscle strength, endurance	emotional stresses
overweight	group dynamics
posture	handling people
sedentariness	mental mechanisms
	motivation

Industrial Physician	*Clinical Psychologist*
2. Physical examinations	2. Personality examinations
special of tired employees	tired employees
annual of all employees	problem employees
	absenteeism
	alcoholics
	nervous
	troublemakers
3. Measure physiological stresses	3. Individual counseling
all heavier jobs	accident prone
all dusty, hot jobs	alcoholics
work methods as needed	nervousness
	personal problems
	relaxing methods
4. Consultant to other departments	4. Consultant to other departments
air conditioning	absenteeism
athletics	incentive plans
lighting	job analysis
noise	job enrichment
recreation	grievances
rest pauses	problem employees
safety	promotion
ventilation	recreation
vibration	safety
work methods	work methods

Men who have the training for these two full-time jobs are in short supply. The annual salary cost for the two would be about equal to the company's last two fringe benefits in the case of a company employing 300.

References cited

The following are sources from which the examples and data and viewpoints given in the book were taken.

Allan, F. N. "The clinical management of weakness and fatigue," *Journal of the Amer. Medical Assn.*, 1945, 127: 957-960.

Bannister, R. G. "Muscular effort," *British Medical Bulletin*, 1956, 12: 222-225.

Bartley, S. H. "Fatigue and inadequacy," *Physiological Review*, 1957, 37: 275-300.

Blackley, C. H. *Experimental Researches on the Causes and Nature of Hay Fever.* London: Baillière, Tindall & Cox. 1873.

Boring, E. G. "Indefatigable scholar," *Contemporary Psychology*, 1959, 4: 385-386.

Bowen, C. D. *Yankee from Olympus.* Boston: Little, Brown & Company. 1944.

Brouha, L. A. "Research on industrial fatigue," *Revue Canadienne de Biologie*, 1948, 7: 479-483.

——— "Fatigue measurement and reduction," *Industrial Medicine & Surgery*, 1953, 22: 547-554.

——— "Physiological approach to problems of work measurement," Proceedings 9th Annual Industrial Engineering Institute, Berkeley, Calif., 1957, pages 12-20.

Burkhardt, E. A. "Fatigue—diagnosis and treatment," *New York State Journal of Medicine*, 1956, 56: 62-67.

Cattell, R. B. *Personality*. New York: McGraw-Hill Book Co. 1950.

—— *Personality and Motivation Structure and Measurement.* Yonkers-on-Hudson: World Book Co. 1957.

—— "Anxiety, extraversion and other second-order personality factors in children," *Journal of Personality*, 1959, 27: 464–476.

Cattell, R. B. and Luborsky, L. B. "P-technique demonstrated as a new clinical method for determining personality and symptom structure," *Journal General Psychology*, 1950, 42: 3–24.

Cattell, R. B. and Scheirer, I. *The Meaning and Measurement of Neuroticism and Anxiety*. New York: Ronald Press Company. 1960.

Clark, L. P. "Lincoln: A Psycho-biography." New York: Charles Scribner's Sons. 1933.

Clarke, H. H. "Strength decrements from wearing various army boots and shoes on military marches," Research Quarterly of the Amer. Assn. for Health, Physical Education and Recreation, 1955, 26: 266–272.

Dill, D. B. "The nature of fatigue," Geriatrics, 1955, 10: 474–478.

Dunlap, J. W. "Men and machines," *Journal of Applied Psychology*, 1947, 31: 565–579.

Edholm, O. G. "Energy expenditure in relation to nutrition," *Proceedings of the Nutrition Society*, 1956, 15: 80–83.

Ffrench, G. E. "The clinical significance of tiredness," *Canadian Medical Association Journal*, 1960, 82: 665–671.

French, G. N. "Some Effects of Physical Training on Breathing, Oxygen Consumption, and Oxygen Extraction during Moderate Exercise." Pensacola, Fla.: U.S. Naval School of Aviation Medicine. 1955 (Research Report No. NM 001 105 100.02).

Gross, I. H. and Bartley, S. H. "Fatigue in house care," *Journal of Applied Psychology*, 1951, 35: 205–207.

Hauty, G. T., et al. "Mitigation of work decrement," *Journal of Experimental Psychology*, 1955, 49: 60–67.

——— "Effects of O_2 and Dextro-amphetamine upon Work Decrement." Randolph Air Force Base, Texas: Air Force School of Aviation Medicine. 1956. Report 56–127.

Haverland, E. M. *An Experimental Analysis by P-technique of some Functional Unitary Varieties of Fatigue.* University of Illinois, Urbana. Library. Ph.D. thesis, 1954.

Hill, S. R. Jr., et al. "Studies on adreno-cortical and psychological response to stress in man," (A.M.A.) *Archives of Internal Medicine*, 1956, 97: 269–298.

Jacques, E. "Fatigue and lowered morale caused by inadequate executive planning," *The Royal Society of Health Journal*, 1958, 78: 513–518.

Kardiner, A. *War Stress and Neurotic Illness.* New York & London: Hoeber. 1947.

Kemble, J. *Napoleon, Immortal.* London: John Murray, Ltd. 1959.

Kempf, E. J. *Psychopathology.* St. Louis: C. V. Mosby Co. 1921.

Kissin, B., et al. "Studies in psychic fatigue. I. Physiologic findings," *Annals of Internal Medicine*, 1957, 46: 274–284

Kleitman, N. *Sleep Characteristics.* Chicago: University of Chicago Press. 1937.

Klumpp, T. G. "Control of fatigue in older persons," *Journal of the American Medical Association*, 1957, 165: 605–607.

Knapp, P. H. "Amphetamine and addiction," *Journal of Nervous & Mental Disease*, 1952, 115: 406–432.

Kraus, H., et al. "Role of inactivity in production of disease," *Journal of The American Geriatrics Society*, 1956, 4: 463–471.

Laughlin, H. P. "The psychiatric aspects of fatigue," *Medical Annals of the District of Columbia*, 1954, 23: 22–37.

——— *The Neuroses in Clinical Practice.* Philadelphia: W. B. Saunders Co. 1956.

Lowenstein, O. "Disintegration of central autonomic regulation during fatigue, etc.," *Journal of Nervous & Mental Disease*, 1952, 115: 1–21; 121–145.

——— "Pupillary reflex shapes and topical clinical diagnosis," *Neurology*, 1955, 5: 631–644.

Muncie, W. "Chronic fatigue," *Psychosomatic Medicine,* 1941, **3**: 277–285.

Muscio, B. "Is a fatigue test possible?" *British Journal of Psychology,* 1921–2, **12**: 31–46.

—— "Feeling-tone in industry," *British Journal of Psychology,* 1921–2, **12**: 151–162.

Neufeld, W. "Relaxation methods in U.S. Navy air schools," *Amer. Journal of Psychiatry,* 1951, **108**: 132–137.

Ogilvie, Sir H. "In praise of idleness," *British Medical Journal,* 1949, **1**: 645–651.

—— "The importance of leisure," *The Practitioner* (London), 1954, **172**: 68–75.

—— *No Miracles among Friends.* London: Max Parrish & Co., Ltd. 1959.

Pearson, R. G. "The Development and Validation of a Checklist for Measuring Subjective Fatigue." Randolph Air Force Base, Texas. Air Force School of Aviation Medicine. 1956. Publication 56–115.

—— "Task Proficiency and Feelings of Fatigue," Randolph Air Force Base, Texas. Air Force School of Aviation Medicine. 1957. Publication 57–77.

Poffenberger, A. "The effects of continuous mental work," *Amer. Journal of Psychology,* 1927, **39**: 283–296.

—— "The effects of continuous mental work upon output and feelings," *Journal of Applied Psychology,* 1928, **12**: 459–467.

Randolph, T. G. "Fatigue and weakness of allergic origin," *Annals of Allergy,* 1945, **3**: 418–460.

—— and Hettig, R. A. "The coincidence of allergic disease, unexplained fatigue, and lymphadenopathy," *Amer. Journal of Medical Science,* 1945, **209**: 306–314.

Romano, J. "Emotional components of illness," *Connecticut State Journal of Medicine,* 1943, **7**: 22–25.

Roush, E. S. "Strength and endurance in waking and hypnotic states, *Journal of Applied Physiology,* 1951, **3**: 404–410.

Sandburg, C. *Abraham Lincoln: The Prairie Years.* New York: Harcourt, Brace and Co., Inc. 1926.

Schwab, R. S. and DeLorno, T. "Psychiatric findings in fatigue," *Amer. Journal of Psychiatry*, 1953, **109**: 621–625.

Shands, H. C. "A note on the significance of fatigue," *Psychosomatic Medicine*, 1952, **14**: 309–314.

Spaulding, W. B. "Fatigue—its clinical significance," *Canadian Medical Association Journal*, 1953, **69**: 570–576.

Speer, F. "Allergic tension-fatigue in children," *Annals of Allergy*, 1954, **12**: 168–171.

——— "The allergic tension-fatigue syndrome," *Pediatric Clinics of North America*, 1954, **1**: 1029–1037.

——— "The allergic tension-fatigue syndrome in children," *Intl. Archives of Allergy and Applied Immunology*, 1958, **12**: 207–214.

Stern, M. H. "Effect of anti-thyroid therapy on objective test performance," *Canadian Journal of Psychology*, 1956, **10**: 226–230.

Thibaut, J. W. and Coules, J. "The role of communication in the reduction of interpersonal hostility," *Journal of Abnormal & Social Psychology*, 1952, **47**: 770–777.

Thorndike, E. L. "Mental fatigue," *Psychological Review*, 1900, **7**: 466–482; 547–579.

Thorndike, R. L. "Normative data obtained in the house-to-house administration of a psychosomatic inventory," *Journal of Consulting Psychology*, 1952, **16**: 257–260.

Wells, J. G., et al. "Lactic acid accumulation during work; a suggested standardization of work classification," *Journal of Applied Physiology*, 1957, **10**: 51–55.

——— "Lactic Acid Accumulation as a Factor in Determining Work Capacity," Randolph Air Force Base, Texas. Air Force School of Aviation Medicine. 1956. Publication 56–121.

Recommended readings

The student, industrial engineer, or other serious reader can get more detail about the problems of tired feelings from these books which deal more intensively with various aspects than the present book does.

There are, unfortunately, very few books devoted primarily to tired feelings, or to fatigue. Those which have current acceptance by scientists are given in the first group.

For the most part, the serious reader will have to glean his additional information from books dealing with other topics but which do bear on tired feelings in one way or another. This requires not only wider reading, which is generally a virtue anyway, but also reading with an active attitude of relating a book's contents to the reader's interest in tired feelings. We have tried to assist in selecting the books by giving a brief description of the contents of each.

In case of difficulty locating a book at a store or library, may we remind you that any public library can borrow a copy for you from another library on interlibrary loan.

I. Books dealing mostly with tiredness

Bartley, S. H. and Chute, E. *Fatigue and Impairment in Man.* New York: McGraw-Hill Book Co., Inc. 1947

> The most complete book dealing exclusively with the problem. Tells in detail why the Old View is being discarded, and points the way for the New View.

Carmichael, L. and Dearborn, W. F. *Reading and Visual Fatigue.*
New York: Houghton Mifflin Company. 1947
  The most thorough study of the book's subject, which found
very little ill-effects from close eye work all day long, even
when conditions for seeing were not favorable by office
standards.

Floyd, W. F. and Welford, A. T. *Symposium on Fatigue.* London: H. K. Lewis & Co. 1953.
  The principal scientists working on problems of tired feelings report what they are doing and finding.

McCormick, E. J. *Human Engineering.* New York: McGraw-
Hill Book Co., Inc. 1957
  A college textbook, of special interest for the material it
contains on designing working equipment so it is easier to use.

II. Biological aspects of tiredness

Cannon, W. B. *The Wisdom of the Body.* New York: W. W.
Norton & Company, Inc. 1932
  An account, by a distinguished physiologist, of the details
by which the body maintains a steady state.

Funkenstein, D. H., et al. *Mastery of Stress.* Cambridge, Mass:
Harvard University Press. 1957
  Report on experiments in which men were subjected to
stress.

Gellhorn, E. *Physiological Foundations of Neurology and Psychiatry.* Minneapolis: University of Minnesota Press. 1953
  Deals with the activities of autonomics and endocrines,
among other things. Not easy to read, but important.

Grinkler, R. R. and Spiegel, J. P. *Men Under Stress.* New York:
Blakiston Division, McGraw-Hill Book Co., Inc. 1945
  Reports of "combat fatigue" from World War II.

Hebb, D. O. *The Organization of Behavior.* New York: John
Wiley & Sons. 1949
  A text dealing with problems of physiological psychology,
and which has had considerable influence in shaping the scientific viewpoint toward tired feelings.

Hess, W. R. *Diencephalon: Autonomic and Extrapyramidal Functions*. New York: Grune & Stratton. 1954

A summary, by a Nobel prize winner, of his discoveries about the role of the autonomic nervous system. Technical reading.

Karpovich, P. V. *Physiology of Muscular Activity*. Philadelphia: W. B. Saunders Company. 1959

The standard text, and easily read as texts go, which should be read by anyone who is working in the field of "fatigue reduction."

Mommaerts, W. F. H. M. *Muscular Contraction*. New York: Interscience Publishers, Inc. 1950

Difficult reading, but the best source for information about the biochemistry of muscular activity and the energy-rich substances which support and maintain the activity.

Selye, H. *The Stress of Life*. New York: McGraw-Hill Book Co., Inc. 1956

By the father of "the stress idea" which has profoundly changed scientific work on tired feelings. A general account of the origin and application of the stress concept.

III. On the "will to work"

Given, W. B., Jr. *Bottom-up Management: People Working Together*. New York: Harper & Brothers. 1953

An account of the author's experiences in sharing management functions with subordinates.

Herzberg, F., et al. *The Motivation to Work*. New York: John Wiley & Sons, Inc. 1959

A study of the motivation of engineers and accountants which leads to a general theory of the will to work.

Lesieur, F. G. (Ed.) *The Scanlon Plan*. New York: John Wiley & Sons, Inc. 1958

A collection of reports on the success of a plan for labor-management cooperation.

Maslow, A. H. *Motivation and Personality*. Harper & Brothers. 1954

A listing and discussion of motives; at present the most widely accepted book on the topic.

Mathewson, S. B. *Restriction of Output among Unorganized Workers*. New York: Viking Press. 1931

The original study which disclosed the great amount of stalling on the job.

Miller, D. C. and Form, W. H. *Industrial Sociology*. New York: Harper & Brothers. 1951

A college textbook which includes material on social influences upon the will to work.

Morse, N. C. *Satisfactions in the White-collar Job*. Ann Arbor, Mich: University of Michigan Press. 1953

What was found among clerks in insurance offices, including their attitudes toward productivity.

Riesman, D. *The Lonely Crowd*. New Haven, Conn: Yale University Press. 1950

An influential book which presents the thesis that the will to work is much different today than a century ago.

Zaleznik, A., et al. *The Motivation, Productivity and Satisfaction of Workers*. Boston: Harvard Graduate School of Business. 1958

The part played by social status and group membership in determining one's will to work.

IV. *The influence of modern situations*

Argyris, C. *Personality and the Organization*. New York: Harper & Brothers. 1957

The conflict between the individual and the modern business organization.

Chinoy, E. *Automobile Workers and the American Dream*. Garden City, N. Y.: Doubleday & Company, Inc. 1955.

A study of the passing of the Horatio Alger era.

Jacques, E. *The Changing Culture of a Factory*. New York: Dryden Press. 1952

What happened to workers' attitudes when a factory changed to a modern style of organization.

March, J. G. *Organizations*. New York: John Wiley & Sons, Inc. 1958

    A text which surveys the various approaches, from Taylorism to modern days.

Roethlisberger, F. J. and Dickson, W. J. *Management and the Worker*. Cambridge, Mass: Harvard University Press. 1947

    A classic which describes the shortcomings of scientific management and points out what are now considered the critical problems.

Walker, C. R. *Toward the Automatic Factory*. New Haven, Conn: Yale University Press. 1957

    Reports on the effects automating had on workers and their organization in one factory.

Walker, C. R. and Guest, R. G. *The Man on the Assembly Line*. Cambridge, Mass: Harvard University Press. 1952

———— *The Foreman on the Assembly Line*. Cambridge, Mass: Harvard University Press. 1956

    Reports studies of workers, and foremen, employed in an automobile assembly plant.

Index

About the Authors

Dr. Donald A. Laird is the author of more than a dozen books on self-improvement subjects and, in recent years, on selling and business techniques. After receiving his Ph.D. degree from the State University of Iowa, Dr. Laird taught psychology at Colgate University and also served as director of the Colgate Psychology Research Laboratory. Eleanor C. Laird, a graduate of Pembroke College, is co-author of *Tired Feelings and How to Master Them, Techniques for Efficient Remembering, Sound Ways to Sound Sleep, The Techniques of Delegating, Sizing Up People,* and several other books.